ENGLISH 3D

S0-AFI-360

LANGUAGE & WRITING
PORTFOLIO
COURSE II

Credits and acknowledgments appear on page 320, which constitutes an extension of this copyright page.

Copyright © 2014 by Scholastic Inc.

All rights reserved.   Published by Scholastic Inc.   Printed in the U.S.A.

ISBN-13: 978-0-545-62975-1
ISBN-10: 0-545-62975-6

SCHOLASTIC, ENGLISH 3D, and associated logos are trademarks and/or registered trademarks of Scholastic Inc. Other company names, brand names, and product names are the property and/or trademarks of their respective owners. Scholastic does not endorse any product or business entity mentioned herein.

Scholastic is constantly working to lessen the environmental impact of our manufacturing processes.
To view our industry-leading paper procurement policy, visit www.scholastic.com/paperpolicy.

1   2   3   4   5   6   7   8   9   10   08   22 21 20 19 18 17 16 15 14 13

Text pages printed on 50% PCW recycled paper.

SCHOLASTIC

TABLE OF
CONTENTS

Welcome to English 3D

Preview the English 3D *Issues by taking this survey. After you complete each Issue, check back to see if your ideas or perspectives have changed.*

1 Teen Sleep

Are you getting enough sleep? Check the box for how many hours you sleep most nights.

- ☐ less than 6 hours
- ☐ 6–7 hours
- ☐ 7–8 hours
- ☐ 8–9 hours
- ☐ more than 9 hours

How many hours of sleep do you think your body needs? _____

2 Learning Languages

Are you taking the classes you need to graduate? Check any of the statements that apply.

- ☐ I don't need to take world languages.
- ☐ I need to take a certain number of credits of world languages.
- ☐ I can earn credits in world languages or another class.
- ☐ I can take a test in my first language instead of taking world languages.
- ☐ I need to take world languages to get into college.

3 Teens Behind the Wheel

Your friend is driving you home after school and starts texting. What would you do? Circle your most likely response.

1. Nothing—my friend is a good driver
2. Refuse a ride from the friend next time
3. Ask if I can send the message for my friend
4. Tell my friend to stop texting
5. Ask my friend to pull over so I can get out

4 Teens & Money

What are your priorities when it comes to money? Number these from most important (1) to least important (5).

_____ Buying clothes, music, or video games

_____ Buying sodas or snacks

_____ Saving for larger purchases like a car or computer

_____ Helping pay family bills

_____ Saving for college

5 Online Learning

How do you use the Internet for learning? Check any of the following statements that apply.

- ☐ Read articles
- ☐ Watch videos
- ☐ Take online classes
- ☐ Research school projects or papers
- ☐ Email teachers about assignments
- ☐ Submit homework
- ☐ Check class websites

6 Ready to Work

List three careers you would like to learn more about.

1. _____
2. _____
3. _____

7 Voting & Citizenship

What do you know about voting in the U.S.? Write T for true and F for false.

_____ People age 17 and older can vote.

_____ Only citizens can vote.

_____ You can choose not to vote.

_____ If you don't vote, you must pay a fine.

8 Failure or Success?

Are successful people born that way or do they have to work hard to get there? Write A if you agree. Write D if you disagree.

_____ Smart people are born smart.

_____ With practice, you can learn to play a sport or an instrument.

_____ If you have to study a lot, then you are not smart.

_____ People who do well in life don't have to work hard.

_____ If you work hard, you can do well in school.

Academic Discussion
WHAT ARE THE CHARACTERISTICS OF AN EFFECTIVE LESSON PARTNER?

 BRAINSTORM IDEAS

Write precise words to discuss and write about the topic.

Everyday	Precise
• smart *(adjective)*	• creative, curious,
• good *(adjective)*	• organized, focused,
• nice *(adjective)*	• respectful, patient,
• fun *(adjective)*	• clever, witty,

 MAKE A CLAIM

Rewrite two ideas using the frame and precise words.

Frame: In my opinion, an effective lesson partner is _____ (**adjective:** prepared, organized) and _____ (**adjective:** respectful, creative)

Response: _____

_____

💬 **COLLABORATE**

Listen attentively, restate, and record your partner's ideas.

Language to RESTATE

So your opinion is that _____.

Yes, that's correct.

No, not exactly. What I meant was _____.

Classmate's Name	Ideas

 PRESENT IDEAS

Listen attentively, compare ideas, and take notes. Then indicate if you agree (+) or disagree (−).

Language to COMPARE IDEAS

My idea is similar to _____'s.

Classmate's Name	Idea	+/−

Words to Go

 BUILD WORD KNOWLEDGE

Complete the meanings and examples for this high-utility academic word.

Word to Go	Meanings	Examples
advantage ad·van·tage *noun*	something that helps you to be better or more _____ ; something that is good or _____ about a place, thing, or situation	In today's multicultural workplace, _____ _____ _____ is an **advantage**. An **advantage** of having a pet is _____

💬 **DISCUSS & WRITE EXAMPLES**

Discuss your response with a partner. Then complete the sentence in writing.

One **advantage** of owning a smart phone is that it allows you to _____

_____

Write your response and read it aloud to a partner.

Having a part-time job is a definite _____ for high school students

who want to _____

💬 **BUILD WORD KNOWLEDGE**

Complete the meaning and examples for this high-utility academic word.

Word to Go	Meaning	Examples
collaborative col·lab·o·ra·tive *adjective*	able to work closely with others to _____ something	Movie awards for _____ _____ are usually won by a **collaborative** team of artists. _____ classes often require more **collaborative** projects than traditional _____ classes.

💬 **DISCUSS & WRITE EXAMPLES**

Discuss your response with a partner. Then complete the sentence in writing.

One advantage of a **collaborative** project is that classmates have the opportunity to

_____

Write your response and read it aloud to a partner.

At home, one _____ chore that we all pitch in on is _____

_____

Language to Summarize

 BUILD FLUENCY

Read the text and prepare to state the key idea.

The Collaborative Advantage

Today, most jobs are too complex to be done by just one person. In the 21st century, a person who knows how to **collaborate**—to work effectively with other people—has a career **advantage**. **Collaboration** is necessary in jobs from construction to retail to medicine.

A medical trauma team is an excellent example of a **collaborative** group. Each team member has a special set of skills and responsibilities. When an accident victim arrives at a hospital, the trauma team has about one hour, known as the golden hour, to save the patient.

A team leader directs about ten doctors, nurses, and support staff. One nurse cuts off the patient's clothes. A trauma doctor examines the patient and makes a diagnosis. The radiologist **contributes** by taking X rays. An anesthesiologist makes sure the patient is breathing and is free from pain. Another nurse calls out the patient's vital signs every five minutes.

The team interacts constantly and works with competence and confidence. No one person could save the patient alone; it takes **collaborative** teamwork.

Not all jobs are a matter of life and death. However, most jobs do require **collaboration**. If you want to succeed in a career, join the team.

 IDENTIFY KEY IDEAS & DETAILS

Take turns asking and answering questions with a partner. Then write brief notes.

Discussion Frames	Text Notes
Q: What is this text **mainly about**? A: This text is **mainly about** _____.	• jobs in which people _____ _____
Q: What are two **important details** in this text? A: One **important detail** in this text is _____. A: Another **important detail** in this text is _____.	• a medical trauma _____ has about an hour to save a _____ • about ten medical _____ collaborate and each team _____ has a job

Academic Discussion
WHAT ARE THE ADVANTAGES AND DISADVANTAGES OF COLLABORATIVE ASSIGNMENTS?

 BRAINSTORM IDEAS

Briefly record at least two ideas in each column using everyday English.

Advantages	Disadvantages
• many ideas to think about	• more ideas to listen to
• could finish faster	• could take longer to finish

 ANALYZE WORDS

Complete the chart with precise verbs to discuss and write about the topic.

> **Language to REPORT**
>
> We would like to suggest the precise verb _____.

Everyday	Precise
get *(verb)*	experience, consider,
finish *(verb)*	accomplish, attain,
deal (with) *(verb)*	tolerate, endure,

MAKE A CLAIM

Rewrite two ideas using the frames and precise words.

1. **Frame:** In my opinion, one potential advantage of working collaboratively is being able to _____ (**base verb:** complete, brainstorm, divide)

   Response: _____

   _____

   _____

2. **Frame:** In my experience, one serious disadvantage of working in some groups is having to _____ (**base verb:** tolerate, consider, handle)

   Response: _____

   _____

   _____

Academic Discussion (continued)

 COLLABORATE

Listen attentively, restate, and record your partner's ideas.

Language to RESTATE

So your (opinion/ experience) is that _____.

Yes, that's correct.

No, not exactly. What I meant was _____.

Classmate's Name	Ideas
	1.
	2.

PRESENT IDEAS

Listen attentively, compare ideas, and take notes. Then indicate if you agree (+) or disagree (−).

Language to COMPARE IDEAS

My (opinion/experience) is similar to _____'s.

Classmate's Name	Idea	+/−

Words to Go

 BUILD WORD KNOWLEDGE

Complete the meanings and examples for this high-utility academic word.

Word to Go	Meanings	Examples
consider con·si·der *verb*	to think about something _____ ; to have an _____ about someone or something	Due to rising gas prices, many commuters are **considering** _____ _____ In my community, many business owners **consider** _____ _____ to be a major problem.

 DISCUSS & WRITE EXAMPLES

Discuss your response with a partner. Then complete the sentence in writing.

When assigning a final grade, I think teachers should **consider** their students'

_____ as well as scores on assignments and tests.

Write your response and read it aloud to a partner.

When I purchase a gift for friends or siblings, two factors I _____

are _____ and _____

BUILD WORD KNOWLEDGE

Complete the meaning and examples for this high-utility academic word.

Word to Go	Meaning	Examples
productive pro·duc·tive *adjective*	_____ a lot	When students have a substitute teacher, they are typically more **productive** if their usual teacher _____ _____ A room with _____ _____ makes studying more **productive** for me.

DISCUSS & WRITE EXAMPLES

Discuss your response with a partner. Then complete the sentence in writing.

When I have an important assignment, I am usually most **productive** working in

_____ because _____

Write your response and read it aloud to a partner.

To have a _____ planning meeting for a school event, classmates

need to _____

Language to Summarize

TAKE A SURVEY
Complete the Classroom Collaboration Survey.

BUILD FLUENCY
Read the article and prepare to state the key idea.

Being a Team Player

Are you a natural team player who enjoys working with others? Or are you a lone wolf who prefers to work independently? No matter what kind of person you are, everyone can strive to be a more effective team member.

A construction crew is a group of people all working for the same goal: to construct a solid building that satisfies a client. However, problems often come up. For example, a construction crew might have to work around a beautiful, old tree that the client wants to save. The backhoe driver cannot move his machine easily around the tree. He wants to bulldoze it down. How can the crew solve this problem?

Productive team members have to express their own ideas clearly and listen attentively to the **perspectives** of others. They have to **consider** other approaches to the problem and be willing to compromise. They have to put the project ahead of their own personal feelings.

In the case of the construction crew, the backhoe driver and the architect compromise to come up with a new solution that saves the tree. No one loses. The team wins.

How was the problem resolved? It took skilled communication and **collaboration**.

IDENTIFY KEY IDEAS & DETAILS
Take turns asking and answering questions with a partner. Then write brief notes.

Discussion Frames	Text Notes
Q: What is this text **mainly about?** A: This text is **mainly about** _____.	• team members who are _____
Q: What are the **most important details** in this text? A: One **important detail** in this text is _____. A: Another **important detail** in this text is _____.	• productive team members have to _____ effectively • working collaboratively also requires being able to _____

Words to Go

BUILD WORD KNOWLEDGE

Complete the meaning and examples for this high-utility academic word.

Word to Go	Meaning	Examples
competent com·pe·tent *adjective*	having enough _____ or knowledge to do something well	Becoming a **competent** soccer player requires _____ Employers often look for job applicants who are **competent** users of _____

DISCUSS & WRITE EXAMPLES

Discuss your response with a partner. Then complete the sentence in writing.

The most reliable way for teens to become **competent** drivers is to _____

_____

because _____

Write your response and read it aloud to a partner.

One of the most noticeable characteristics of a _____ leader is

the ability to _____

BUILD WORD KNOWLEDGE

Complete the meaning and examples for this high-utility academic word.

Word to Go	Meaning	Examples
complex com·plex *adjective*	having many parts or details and often _____ to understand	The rules of some video games are too **complex** for most _____ Science textbooks tend to be more **complex** than other books because they include a lot of _____

DISCUSS & WRITE EXAMPLES

Discuss your response with a partner. Then complete the sentence in writing.

Adults often have to ask children for assistance with using _____

_____ because they can be quite **complex**.

Write your response and read it aloud to a partner.

From my perspective, _____ is a musician who sings interesting

and **complex** lyrics, such as those in the song _____

Language to Summarize

BUILD FLUENCY

Read the article and prepare to state the key idea.

The Importance of Face-to-Face Communication

You can probably text, email, blog, and tweet without a problem. But are you equally comfortable with face-to-face communication? Working with a team requires a great deal of face time with other team members. **Collaboration** is challenging if you are not sure how to communicate.

How do **competent** communicators behave? Here is an example. A school club wants to sell snacks at a weekend event. Some members of the club want to sell junk food because kids like it. Others want to try healthier alternatives. Each group presents its side of the issue at a meeting.

When the first side speaks, the team members present facts as well as feelings. They give reasons and evidence for their **perspectives**. Their body language is calm and confident. As the the second side listens, take notes and look for ideas that they/its members agree with as well as disagree with. They respond with questions and their own opinions. They do not react with feelings and criticism. They do not explode, shut down, or ridicule.

The communication leads to a compromise that satisfies both sides. The club members avoid conflict. Communication helps the team work **productively** and find the best solution.

Use these tips for successful teamwork:

- Present your ideas effectively.
- Listen attentively to others' ideas.
- Prepare to compromise to solve **complex** problems.
- Remember your team's goal—and make it a success.

ASK & ANSWER QUESTIONS

Take turns asking and answering questions with a partner. Then write brief notes.

Discussion Frames	Text Notes
Q: What is this text **mainly about?** **A:** This text is **mainly about** _____.	• in-person _____
Q: What are the **most important details in this text?** **A:** (One/Another) **important detail in this text** is _____.	• competent communicators remain _____ and don't insult people who _____ • compromising can _____ complex _____

Academic Discussion

IS TECHNOLOGY NEGATIVELY AFFECTING TEEN COMMUNICATION?

 BRAINSTORM IDEAS

Briefly record at least two ideas in each column using everyday English.

Agree	Disagree
• use short sentences when texting	• gets teens chatting with people they wouldn't have the chance to normally

ANALYZE WORDS

Complete the chart with precise adjectives to discuss and write about the issue.

> **Language to REPORT**
>
> We would like to suggest the precise adjective _____.

Everyday	Precise
quick *(adjective)*	efficient, immediate,
boring *(adjective)*	inefficient, tedious,
casual *(adjective)*	informal, common,
fancy *(adjective)*	formal, appropriate,

MAKE A CLAIM

Rewrite one idea using the frame and a precise adjective.

Frame: In my opinion, _____ (**form of technology:** texting, social networking, email) has made teen communication _____ (more/less) (**adjective:** effective, impressive, precise, informal)

Response: _____

_____

_____

Academic Discussion (continued)

 COLLABORATE

Listen attentively, restate, and record your partner's idea.

Classmate's Name	Idea

Language to RESTATE

So your perspective is that _____.

Yes, that's correct.

No, not exactly. What I meant was _____.

PRESENT IDEAS

Listen attentively, compare ideas, and take notes. Then indicate whether you agree (+) or disagree (–).

Language to AGREE/DISAGREE

I (agree/disagree) with _____'s perspective that _____.

Classmate's Name	Idea	+/–

Ten-Minute Paper

A **ten-minute paper** begins with a well-stated **claim,** followed by **two detail sentences** that elaborate with relevant examples and precise words.

ELABORATE IN WRITING
Read and analyze the teacher's ten-minute paper. Circle three precise adjectives.

Language to COLLABORATE

What should we write?

We could put _____. What do you think makes sense?

We could also write _____.

> In my opinion, email has made teen communication more efficient. For example, if absent students have questions about a major assignment, they can quickly send a message to a responsible classmate instead of interrupting his or her studies with a phone call. As a result, the classmate can simply reply with a brief message explaining the homework instructions rather than taking the time to go into extensive detail in a phone conversation.

Work with the teacher to write a ten-minute paper. Include two precise adjectives.

> In my opinion, texting has made teen communication less precise. For example, texting requires use of _____ vocabulary that everyone will understand and abbreviations for _____ expressions, such as _____ for _____
> As a result, English teachers have noticed an increase in inappropriate _____ , spelling _____ , and texting expressions in their students' formal _____

Work with a partner to write a ten-minute paper. Include two precise adjectives.

> In my opinion, _____ has made teen communication
> (less/more) _____ (adjective) _____
> For example, _____
> _____
> _____
> As a result, _____
> _____
> _____

Do TEENS NEED A WAKE-UP CALL WHEN IT COMES TO SLEEP?

BUILD KNOWLEDGE
Read and respond to the Data File (*Issues*, p. 4).

BRAINSTORM IDEAS
Write a brief list of reasons why teens stay up late.

- doing household chores
- _____

- _____
- _____

PRESENT IDEAS
Use the frames to discuss ideas with your group. Listen attentively and record the strongest ideas to complete the concept web.

> **Language to FACILITATE DISCUSSION**
> So _____, what's your experience?
> _____, what reason did you come up with?

1. Some teens stay up late because they are _____ (**verb** + *-ing*: completing)

2. Teens might also stay up late _____ (**verb** + *-ing*: worrying about)

3. Sometimes I (have to/decide to) stay up late _____ (**verb** + *-ing*: reading)

4. I occasionally have to stay up late _____ (**verb** + *-ing*: studying for)

- writing essays
- studying for test
- having stress
- playing video games
- helping parents
- having consequence

REASONS TEENS STAY UP LATE

Words to Know

 BUILD WORD KNOWLEDGE

Rate your word knowledge. Then discuss word meanings and examples with your group.

	① Don't Know	② Recognize	③ Familiar	④ Know

Word to Know	Meaning	Examples
1 adolescent noun ① ② ③ ④	a young person who is becoming an adult; _teenager_	Many **adolescents** like to _hang out with friends_ _____ after school.
2 stage noun ① ② ③ ④	a particular _time_ _or stage_ that something reaches as it grows or develops	My 16-month-old sister has reached the **stage** of life where she is _crawling on the floor._
3 sleep-deprived adjective ① ② ③ ④	lacking the _sleep_ needed over a period of time	When my baby brother was born, my parents were so **sleep-deprived** that they _have to take care of the baby._
4 puberty noun ① ② ③ ④	the time when a person's body changes _from a child to an adult_	During **puberty**, teens often have to start _speaking approprite and knowing more things about life._
1 deficit noun ① ② ③ ④	the difference between how much _you have_ _____ and how much _need_	Our team needed to overcome a **deficit** of _number of player in our team,_ to win the championship game.
2 hormone noun ① ② ③ ④	chemicals _in the body_ that affect how it grows and develops	Sometimes **hormones** can make teens _group up and become an adult._
3 metabolism noun ① ② ③ ④	the process in the body that _changes food into energy_ for working and growing	When you _shave all the foods in your body_ your **metabolism** is higher because your body needs more energy.
4 symptom noun ① ② ③ ④	something wrong with your _body or mind_ that shows you are ill	**Symptoms** of the flu include _sneezing coughing and chinese eyes_

Academic Discussion

WHAT ARE SOME REASONS WHY ADOLESCENTS FAIL TO GET SUFFICIENT SLEEP?

BRAINSTORM IDEAS

Briefly record at least two ideas in each column using everyday English.

Personal Reasons	Environmental Reasons
• dealing with social problems	• noisy traffic outside
•	•
•	•

ANALYZE WORDS

Complete the chart with … the topic.

Everyday		
problems *(plural noun)*		ment,
work *(noun)*		manual labor
finish *(verb)*		

① issues, despair, questions, struggles stress.
② job, progress, process.
③ conclude, summarize, terminate end.

MAKE A CLAIM

Rewrite two ideas using … Then prepare to elabora…

1. **Frame:** I know from ex… fail to get adequate sleep during the school week because they stay up late ______ (**verb + *-ing***: revising essays for English class, reading novels)

   Response: listening to some dubstep music

2. **Frame:** Based on my experience, adolescents fail to get sufficient sleep on school nights because of ______ (**noun phrase**: social issues, lengthy homework assignments)

   Response: doing summarize for the essay.

…age to ELABORATE

…mple, ______.

…this firsthand because ______.

COLLABORATE

Listen attentively, restate, and record your partner's ideas.

Classmate's Name	Ideas
	1.
	2.

Language to RESTATE

So you believe that ______.

Yes, that's correct.

No, not exactly. What I (pointed out/stated) was ______.

Ten-Minute Paper

A **ten-minute paper** begins with a well-stated **claim,** followed by **two detail sentences** that elaborate with relevant examples and precise words.

Language to AGREE/DISAGREE

I agree with _____'s idea.

I don't quite agree with _____'s idea.

 PRESENT IDEAS

Listen attentively and take notes. Then indicate if you agree (+) or disagree (–).

Classmate's Name	Idea	+/–
Hamud	Stay up late watching movie	
Kevin	Doing classwork or homework	
Jesus	Stay up late playing video games	

ELABORATE IN WRITING

Work with the teacher to write a ten-minute paper.

Language to COLLABORATE

What should we write?

We could put _____. What do you think makes sense?

We could also write _____.

I know from experience that many adolescents fail to get adequate sleep during the school week because they stay up late completing various homework assignments. For example, I recently studied well past midnight because I had to read an entire history ___chapter___ and take notes, prepare for an exam in ___history class___ and finish editing a ___essay for history___ _____ As a result, I only got ___5___ hours of sleep and I felt ___exhausted___ and ___sleepy___ during my morning classes.

Work with a partner to write a ten-minute paper.

I know from experience that many adolescents fail to get adequate sleep during the school week because they stay up late ___Studying for science___ _____ For example, I regularly fall asleep no earlier than ___2 hours after bed time___ because I spend several hours ___Studying for science and doing home work___ As a result, I have a great deal of trouble staying awake and ___I feel___ ___sleep-deprived___ the next school day, especially in challenging classes such as ___science and writing.___

Words to Go

BUILD WORD KNOWLEDGE

Complete the meanings and examples for these high-utility academic words.

Words to Go	Meanings	Examples
tend to tend to *verb*	to be likely to _act or think_ a certain way	If I am nervous about making a presentation in class, I **tend to** _calm down and slowly present in class_
tendency ten·den·cy *noun*	part of your character that makes you likely to act or think _a certain way_	Students have a **tendency** to _mess around_ ____ when there is a substitute teacher.

DISCUSS & WRITE EXAMPLES

Discuss your response with a partner. Then complete the sentence in writing.

My English teacher **tends to** reward students who have completed their assignments well with _foods_

Write your response and read it aloud to a partner.

The coach's ___ _tendency_ ___ to _not doing his part_ ___

during games made him unpopular with many athletes and parents.

BUILD WORD KNOWLEDGE

Complete the meaning and examples for this high-utility academic word.

Word to Go	Meaning	Examples
consequence con·se·quence *noun*	something that happens because of an _action_	The **consequence** of not doing my homework was _getting a bad grade._ He _didn't do his homework_ ___ so now he must face the **consequences**.

DISCUSS & WRITE EXAMPLES

Discuss your response with a partner. Then complete the sentence in writing.

When I ate a large snack after school, the **consequence** was _getting an ill_

Write your response and read it aloud to a partner.

The ___ _consequence_ ___ of preparing my presentation in advance and practicing it several times in front of ___ _the whole class_ ___ was that I

____

Close Reading

 BUILD FLUENCY

Read the text "Who Needs Sleep?" (*Issues*, pp. 5–8).

 IDENTIFY KEY IDEAS & DETAILS

Take turns asking and answering questions with a partner. Then write brief notes.

Discussion Frames	Text Notes
Q: What is the **key idea** of this text? A: The **key idea** of this text is ____.	• sleep _____ to adolescent health, but teens don't get enough
Q: What are the **most important details** in this text? A: (One/Another) **important detail** in this text is ____.	• 5 sleep stages: need sleeping/dreaming to _____ • teens sleep average of ____ hrs. a night; need 9+ • teen body's _____ is pushed back; doesn't feel _____ until _____ • chronic _____ causes serious health issues: depressed mood, weakened _____ weight gain

 RESPOND WITH EVIDENCE

Use the frame and evidence from the text to construct a formal written response.

1. According to the author, what are some physical consequences of inadequate sleep?

   According to the author, _____

   are physical consequences of inadequate sleep. In addition, accumulating a sleep deficit

   can lead to _____

Use the frame to analyze the author's word choice.

2. What is the effect of describing teenagers as "walking zombies" on page 7?

   One effect of describing teenagers as "walking zombies" is to compare _____

   _____

   Zombies are _____

   Describing sleep-deprived adolescents as "walking zombies" suggests that teens

   _____

IDENTIFY PRECISE WORDS

Review Text 1 and your *Portfolio* (pp. 18–23) to identify words for your writing.

Topic Words	High-Utility Academic Words
• sleep-debt	• adequate
•	•
•	•

Academic Discussion
WHAT ARE THE CONSEQUENCES OF SLEEP DEPRIVATION?

 BRAINSTORM IDEAS

Briefly record at least two ideas in each column using everyday English.

Physical Consequences	Mental Consequences
• getting out of shape	• less interest in friends
•	•
•	•

 ANALYZE WORDS

Complete the chart with precise words to discuss and write about the issue.

Everyday	Precise
often *(adverb)*	regularly,
tired *(adjective)*	fatigued,
moody *(adjective)*	antisocial,

 MAKE A CLAIM

Rewrite two ideas using the frames and precise words. Then prepare to elaborate verbally.

Language to ELABORATE

For example, _____.

I know this firsthand because _____.

1. **Frame:** One physical (consequence/impact/outcome) of sleep deprivation for adolescents is _____ (**verb + –ing:** having, getting, gaining)

   Response: _____

   _____

2. **Frame:** A mental (consequence/impact/outcome) of chronic fatigue is that adolescents can become _____ (**adjective:** distracted, alienated, antisocial)

   Response: _____

   _____

 COLLABORATE

Listen attentively, restate, and record your partner's ideas.

Language to RESTATE

So you believe that _____.

Yes, that's correct.

No, not exactly. What I (pointed out/stated) was _____.

Classmate's Name	Ideas
	1.
	2.

Ten-Minute Paper

A **ten-minute paper** begins with a well-stated **claim,** followed by **two detail sentences** that elaborate with relevant examples and precise words.

PRESENT IDEAS

Listen attentively, and take notes. Then indicate if you agree (+) or disagree (–).

Classmate's Name	Idea	+/–

ELABORATE IN WRITING

Work with the teacher to write a ten-minute paper.

One _____ consequence of sleep deprivation for adolescents is getting sick _____ For example, not getting _____ sleep throughout the week weakens an individual's immune system. As a result, _____ teens commonly develop illnesses such as _____ and _____ and have to miss _____ days of school.

Work with your partner to write a ten-minute paper.

A _____ impact of chronic fatigue is that adolescents can become forgetful. For example, insufficient sleep can cause _____ with short-term memory and _____ As a result, teens who _____ come to school feeling _____ have considerable difficulty _____ _____

Words to Go

 BUILD WORD KNOWLEDGE

Complete the meaning and examples for this high-utility academic word.

Word to Go	Meaning	Examples
affect af·fect *verb*	to _change_ someone or something	_Catching up my work_ would positively **affect** my grades. _after taking a shower would_ _____ **affects** what I decide to wear in the morning.

DISCUSS & WRITE EXAMPLES

Discuss your response with a partner. Then complete the sentence in writing.

When buying a new cell phone, _the system inside the cell phone_

is likely to **affect** an adolescent customer's decision.

Write your response and read it aloud to a partner.

High School diploma and grades,

will _affect_ my success after high school.

BUILD WORD KNOWLEDGE

Complete the meaning and examples for this high-utility academic word.

Word to Go	Meaning	Examples
factor fac·tor *noun*	One of the things that _causes a result_	A **factor** in the family's decision to move was _their hometown really is messy and noisy._ Eating a healthy breakfast is a **factor** in _the morning / helping me walking to school._

DISCUSS & WRITE EXAMPLES

Discuss your response with a partner. Then complete the sentence in writing.

irresponsible parents is is a

factor that contributes to the problem of teen drug use.

Write your response and read it aloud to a partner.

Two _factors_ that I consider when choosing a book to read are

pictures and _short chapters._

Section Shrink

BUILD FLUENCY

Read the introduction and Section 1 of "Sleep Is One Thing Missing in Busy Teenage Lives" (*Issues*, pp. 9–12).

IDENTIFY KEY IDEAS & DETAILS

Take turns asking and answering questions with a partner. Then write brief notes.

Discussion Frames	Text Notes
Q: What is the **key idea** of this section? **A:** The **key idea** of this section is _____.	• teens are often _____ on school days
Q: What are the **most important details** in this section? **A:** (One/Another) **important detail** in this section is _____. **A:** Perhaps the **most important detail** in this section is _____.	• internal clock _____ so teens fall asleep later and wake up early feeling _____ • physical consequences: _____ impaired immune system, risk of _____ _____ and _____ • mental consequences: memory lapses, trouble _____ moodiness, _____

SUMMARIZE

"Shrink" Section 1 of the text by writing a summary in 40 or fewer words.

CLASS SUMMARY   **WORD COUNT:** _____

Many adolescents are _____ at school because their _____ are off, making them regularly fall asleep late and get less than _____ hours of sleep per night, resulting in a number of _____ and emotional _____.

PARTNER SUMMARY   **WORD COUNT:** _____

Many adolescents are typically _____ during the school week because their internal clocks _____ making them feel _____ instead of _____ and this can lead to _____ with their _____ and _____.

IDENTIFY PRECISE WORDS

Review Section 1 and your *Portfolio* (pp. 24–27) to identify words for your writing.

Topic Words	High-Utility Academic Words
• sleep-deprived	• consequence
•	•
•	•

Words to Go

 BUILD WORD KNOWLEDGE

Complete the meanings and examples for these high-utility academic words.

Words to Go	Meanings	Examples
respond re·spond *verb*	to_____ to something that has been said or done	After seeing destruction caused by the hurricane, people **responded** by _____ _____
response re·sponse *noun*	a _____ to something that has been said or done	The principal's decision to allow _____ _____ elicited an enthusiastic student **response**.

 DISCUSS & WRITE EXAMPLES

Discuss your response with a partner. Then complete the sentence in writing.

If I found out that I had won the state lottery and become a multimillionaire, I would

respond by _____

Write your response and read it aloud to a partner.

When high school students have a major writing assignment, a common

_____ is to _____

_____

 BUILD WORD KNOWLEDGE

Complete the meaning and examples for this high-utility academic word.

Word to Go	Meaning	Examples
survey sur·vey *verb*	to _____ many people the same questions to find out their opinions	I would enjoy **surveying** my classmates about _____ _____ A new business might want to **survey** people who _____ _____

 DISCUSS & WRITE EXAMPLES

Discuss your response with a partner. Then complete the sentence in writing.

If our school **surveyed** students about changes they want at our school, it would probably

find that many want _____

Write your response and read it aloud to a partner.

Before organizing an end-of-the-year party, I would _____

classmates to find out _____

_____

Section Shrink

 BUILD FLUENCY

Read Section 2 of "Sleep Is One Thing Missing in Busy Teenage Lives"
(*Issues*, pp. 12–13).

 IDENTIFY KEY IDEAS & DETAILS

Take turns asking and answering questions with a partner. Then write brief notes.

Discussion Frames	Text Notes
Q: What is the **key idea** of this section? **A:** The **key idea** of this section is _____.	• changing school _____
Q: What are the **most important details** in this section? **A:** (One/Another) **important detail** in this section is _____. **A:** Perhaps the **most important detail** in this section is _____.	• sleep foundation says schools should start at _____ • schools that changed times have better _____ and _____ • reasons against changing times: _____ _____ • after-school _____

 SUMMARIZE

"Shrink" Section 2 of the text by writing a summary in 40 or fewer words.

CLASS SUMMARY   **WORD COUNT:** _____

High schools have found that making the school day start _____

can _____ attendance and _____

but some people want to keep _____ start times because of bus

_____ and _____ activities.

PARTNER SUMMARY   **WORD COUNT:** _____

While _____ high school start times has improved

_____ and graduation rates, _____

want to keep earlier start times due to _____

with bus schedules and student participation in _____

_____

 IDENTIFY PRECISE WORDS

Review Section 2 and your *Portfolio* (pp. 28–29) to identify words for your writing.

Topic Words	High-Utility Academic Words
• attendance • •	• survey • •

Words to Go

 BUILD WORD KNOWLEDGE

Complete the meaning and examples for this high-utility academic word.

Word to Go	Meaning	Examples
approach ap·proach *noun*	a _____ of doing something	My **approach** to preparing for a test is to _____ _____ During a job interview, _____ _____ is definitely the wrong **approach**.

💬 **DISCUSS & WRITE EXAMPLES**

Discuss your response with a partner. Then complete the sentence in writing.

One **approach** for dealing with an argument with a friend is _____

_____

Write your response and read it aloud to a partner.

An effective _____ to getting a curfew extension might be

_____

 BUILD WORD KNOWLEDGE

Complete the meaning and examples for this high-utility academic word.

Word to Go	Meaning	Examples
data da·ta *noun*	information or _____	A research paper about teen driving habits might include **data** about _____ _____ _____ Before purchasing a car for an adolescent driver, a parent should gather **data** on _____ _____

💬 **DISCUSS & WRITE EXAMPLES**

Discuss your response with a partner. Then complete the sentence in writing.

Useful **data** for choosing a place to take a vacation might include _____

_____

Write your response and read it aloud to a partner.

Before applying to a particular college or trade school, I would review

_____ on _____

Section Shrink

BUILD FLUENCY

Read Section 3 of "Sleep Is One Thing Missing in Busy Teenage Lives"
(*Issues*, pp. 14–15).

IDENTIFY KEY IDEAS & DETAILS

Take turns asking and answering questions with a partner. Then write brief notes.

Discussion Frames	Text Notes
Q: What is the **key idea** of this section? **A:** The **key idea** of this section is _____.	• Navy _____ _____
Q: What are the **most important details** in this section? **A:** (One/Another) **important detail** in this section is _____. **A:** Perhaps the **most important detail** in this section is _____.	• changed "rack time" to _____ but recruits couldn't _____ that early • new "rack time" is _____ • Navy studying whether it improves test _____ • mental consequences: memory lapses, moodiness, trouble _____ _____

SUMMARIZE

"Shrink" Section 3 of the text by writing a summary in 40 or fewer words.

CLASS SUMMARY   **WORD COUNT:** _____

The Navy changed its "rack time" to _____ so _____

can get _____ hours of sleep per night, and it is _____

whether it improves behavior and _____

PARTNER SUMMARY   **WORD COUNT:** _____

The new Navy _____ is 10 p.m. to 6 a.m., which allows sailors

to _____ eight hours per night, and the Navy is collecting

_____ about whether the sleep schedule

_____ test scores and _____

IDENTIFY PRECISE WORDS

Review Section 3 and your *Portfolio* (pp. 30–31) to identify words for your writing.

Topic Words	High-Utility Academic Words
• psychologists	• data
•	•
•	•

Student Writing Model

Academic Writing Type

A **formal written summary** provides an objective overview of the topic and important details from an informational text. The writer credits the author, but writes in primarily his or her own words, without including personal opinions.

- A. The **topic sentence** includes the text type, title, author, and topic.
- B. **Detail sentences** include the important details from the summarized text.
- C. The **concluding sentence** restates the author's conclusion in the writer's own words.

ANALYZE TEXT

Read this student model to analyze the elements of a formal summary.

> **A** In the magazine article titled "Who Needs Sleep?," Kristen Weir investigates why sleep is so crucial for teens. **B** First, Weir reports that 60 percent of middle and high school students say that they experience chronic fatigue at school. The author also explains that teens should average nine or more hours of sleep a night, but most tend to get about seven. In addition, she clarifies that this adolescent sleep deficit is due to numerous factors, such as busy schedules and a shift during puberty in the body's internal clock. Furthermore, the author describes multiple consequences of being sleep-deprived, such as issues with digestion and memory. **C** Finally, Weir concludes that teens should make sure they regularly get sufficient sleep to stay healthy and happy.

MARK & DISCUSS ELEMENTS

Mark the summary elements and use the frames to discuss them with your partner.

1. **Number (1–4) the four elements of the topic sentence.**
   The topic sentence includes the _____.

2. **Draw a box around four transition words or phrases.**
   One transition (word/phrase) is _____.

3. **Underline four important details.** *One important detail in this summary is _____.*

4. **Circle four citation verbs.** *One citation verb that the writer uses is _____.*

5. **Star four precise topic words and check four high-utility academic words.**
   An example of a (precise topic word/high-utility academic word) is _____.

Paraphrasing Text

Guidelines for Paraphrasing a Sentence

Paraphrase one sentence from a source text by keeping important topic words and replacing key words and phrases with synonyms.

Source Text	Key Words & Phrases → Synonyms		Paraphrasing
"Most are lucky to get six, seven, or eight hours of sleep a night, even though studies have shown repeatedly that people in their teens and possibly even early 20's need nine to 10 hours" (Grady 9).	most [teens]	→ adolescents	Adolescents tend to only sleep eight or fewer hours per night although research often demonstrates they actually need nine to 10 hours.
	are lucky to get	→ tend to only sleep	
	six, seven, or eight hours	→ eight or fewer hours	
	even though studies have shown	→ although research demonstrates	
	repeatedly	→ often	

IDENTIFY PRECISE SYNONYMS

Read these statements and replace the words in parentheses with synonyms.

1. Tired students have (a hard time) _____ paying attention, and even if they do somehow manage to focus, they may (forget) _____ _____ what they were taught because memory formation takes place partly during sleep.

2. Some school districts have already (changed) _____ their schedules so that high school classes (start) _____ later, between 8 and 9, instead of before 8.

3. Navy researchers are (studying) _____ the (sailors) _____ to see if the extra sleep makes a difference.

PARAPHRASE IDEAS

Paraphrase the three statements from above using primarily your own words.

1. Shellenbarger reports that _____
   _____
   _____

2. The author explains that _____
   _____
   _____

3. She describes how _____
   _____
   _____

Nouns & Pronouns to Credit an Author

Guidelines to Credit an Author

Topic Sentence: State the author's full name.

1st Important Detail: State the author's last name.

2nd Important Detail: Use the term *author, writer,* or *researcher.*

3rd Important Detail: Use the pronoun *he* or *she.*

4th Important Detail: Use the term *author, writer,* or *researcher.*

Concluding Sentence: Use the author's last name.

 IDENTIFY NOUNS & PRONOUNS

Read the summary and circle the nouns and pronouns that credit the author.

> In the news story titled "Falling Asleep in Class? Blame Biology," Madison Park discusses why adolescents have difficulty getting adequate sleep. First, Park points out that teens' body clocks conflict with high school schedules. The writer also reports that a Kentucky district altered its high school start time to 8:30 a.m., and half of students surveyed said they were sleeping eight hours per night. In addition, she explains that later start times can reduce car accidents and improve attendance. Furthermore, the writer points out that the glow of technological devices such as cell phones and computer screens can make falling asleep more difficult. Finally, Park concludes that schools should also consider parents' and employers' points of view before changing schedules.

 TAKE NOTES

Write nouns and pronouns to credit the author in your formal summary of Text 2.

Summary Sentence	Noun/Pronoun to Credit the Author
Topic Sentence	
1st Detail	
2nd Detail	
3rd Detail	
4th Detail	
Concluding Sentence	

Organize a Formal Summary

Prompt Write a formal summary of "Sleep Is One Thing Missing in Busy Teenage Lives."

Guidelines for Paraphrasing Multiple Sentences

Paraphrase related details from a source text by combining key information into one sentence. Replace key words and phrases with synonyms and keep important topic words.

Text Detail 1	Text Detail 2	Text Detail 3
"… tired students have a hard time paying attention, and even if they do somehow manage to focus, they may forget what they were taught" (Grady 10).	"Dr. Carskadon said studies had repeatedly linked sleep deprivation to depressed mood—a temporary case of the blues" (Grady 11).	"Lack of sleep also increases teenage drivers' already elevated risk of car accidents" (Grady 12).

PARAPHRASE IDEAS

Combine key information from the three text details above into one detail sentence.

There are physical and mental impacts of sleep deprivation, including

(Text Detail 1) _____

(Text Detail 2) _____ and

(Text Detail 3) _____

PLAN KEY IDEAS & DETAILS

State the text information to write a topic sentence.

In the news article titled (title) _____

_____

(author's full name) _____ (citation verb: explores, examines, discusses)

_____ (topic) _____

List four important details from the article using primarily your own words.

1. _____

_____

2. _____

_____

3. _____

_____

4. _____

_____

Restate the author's conclusion in your own words.

_____

_____

Write a Formal Summary

Prompt Write a formal summary of "Sleep Is One Thing Missing in Busy Teenage Lives."

 WRITE A PARAGRAPH
Use the frame to write your topic sentence, detail sentences, and concluding sentence.

A

In the magazine article titled _____
_____ (title)

_____   _____
(author's full name)   (citation verb)

_____
(topic)

B

First, _____ explains _____
      (author's last name)   (1st important detail)

_____

_____

The (author/writer/researcher) _____ also reports

(2nd important detail)
_____

_____

In addition, (he/she) _____ describes _____
                                                          (3rd important detail)
_____

_____

Furthermore, the (author/writer/researcher) _____ points out

(4th important detail)
_____

_____

C

Finally, _____ concludes that _____
       (author's last name)   (restate author's conclusion)
_____

Rate Your Summary

ASSESS YOUR DRAFT

Rate your formal summary. Then have a partner rate it.

Scoring Guide	
1	Insufficient
2	Developing
3	Sufficient
4	Exemplary

		1	2	3	4
1. Does the topic sentence state the title, author, and topic?	Self	1	2	3	4
	Partner	1	2	3	4
2. Did you paraphrase the most important details from the text?	Self	1	2	3	4
	Partner	1	2	3	4
3. Did you include precise topic words and high-utility academic words?	Self	1	2	3	4
	Partner	1	2	3	4
4. Did you restate the author's conclusion using your own words?	Self	1	2	3	4
	Partner	1	2	3	4

REFLECT & REVISE

Record specific priorities and suggestions to help you and your partner revise.

(Partner) Positive Feedback: I appreciate how you (used/included) _____

_____

_____

(Partner) Suggestion: As you revise your summary, focus on _____

_____

_____

(Self) Priority 1: My summary paragraph needs _____

_____

_____

(Self) Priority 2: I plan to improve my summary by _____

_____

_____

CHECK & EDIT

Use this checklist to proofread and edit your formal summary.

☐ Did you capitalize the title of the article and proper nouns?

☐ Did you put quotation marks around the title of the article?

☐ Is each sentence complete?

☐ Are all words spelled correctly?

Academic Discussion
HOW CAN ADOLESCENTS ENSURE THEY GET ADEQUATE SLEEP?

 BRAINSTORM IDEAS

Briefly record at least two ideas in each column using everyday English.

Healthy Habits	Activities
• don't drink caffeine after noon	• go to sleep by 11:00
•	•
•	•

 ANALYZE WORDS

Complete the chart with precise words to discuss and write about the topic.

Everyday	Precise
try to *(verb)*	attempt to,
stop *(verb)*	refrain from,
change *(verb)*	alter,

 MAKE A CLAIM

Rewrite two ideas using the frames and precise words. Then prepare to elaborate verbally.

1. **Frame:** In order to ensure adequate sleep on school nights, adolescents should _____ (**base verb:** avoid, exercise, attempt to)

   Response: _____

   _____

2. **Frame:** Based on my experience, one way adolescents can ensure adequate sleep during the school week is by _____ (**verb + –ing:** altering, completing, improving)

   Response: _____

   _____

 COLLABORATE

Listen attentively, restate, and record your partner's ideas.

Classmate's Name	Ideas
	1.
	2.

Ten-Minute Paper

A **ten-minute paper** begins with a **claim,** followed by **two detail sentences** that elaborate with relevant examples and precise words.

Language to AGREE/DISAGREE

I agree with _____'s idea.

I don't quite agree with _____'s idea.

 PRESENT IDEAS

Listen attentively and take notes. Then indicate if you agree (+) or disagree (–).

Classmate's Name	Idea	+/–

ELABORATE IN WRITING

Work with the teacher to write a ten-minute paper.

Language to COLLABORATE

What should we write?

We could put _____. What do you think makes sense?

We could also write _____.

In order to ensure adequate sleep on school nights, adolescents should strive to maintain a regular sleep schedule. For example, teens can start winding down at _____ p.m., turn off the lights by _____ p.m., and refrain from responding to _____ As a result, their internal clock will adjust to the new _____ and they will have an easier time _____ _____

Work with your partner to write a ten-minute paper.

Based on my experience, one way adolescents can ensure adequate sleep during the school week is by avoiding using bright technology before bedtime. For example, teens need to stop using their _____ and _____ before going to sleep and make sure their _____ are turned off. As a result, they will not be tempted to _____ and will instead wind down and improve their _____ _____

Words to Go

 BUILD WORD KNOWLEDGE

Complete the meaning and examples for this high-utility academic word.

Word to Go	Meaning	Examples
trend trend *noun*	a general direction in which things are _____	A growing workplace **trend** is to _____ _____ instead of making phone calls. A popular **trend** in 21st century learning is offering _____

 DISCUSS & WRITE EXAMPLES

Discuss your response with a partner. Then complete the sentence in writing.

A recent **trend** in teen fashion is wearing _____

_____

Write your response and read it aloud to a partner.

There is an increasing _____ in the number of car accidents due to people who _____ at the wheel.

 BUILD WORD KNOWLEDGE

Complete the meaning and examples for this high-utility academic word.

Word to Go	Meaning	Examples
regulate reg·u·late *verb*	to manage or _____ especially by rules	Teens with demanding schedules need to **regulate** the amount of time spent _____ because it takes too long. The government **regulates** the speed limits near schools to _____ _____

 DISCUSS & WRITE EXAMPLES

Discuss your response with a partner. Then complete the sentence in writing.

High schools **regulate** the _____

and _____ you need to graduate.

Write your response and read it aloud to a partner.

Dentists recommend that parents _____ the amount of _____ and _____ that children consume to reduce cavities.

Close Reading

BUILD FLUENCY
Read the text "Understanding the Zombie Teen's Body Clock" (*Issues*, pp. 16–19).

IDENTIFY KEY IDEAS & DETAILS
Take turns asking and answering questions with a partner. Then write brief notes.

Discussion Frames	Text Notes
Q: What is the **key idea** of this text? **A:** The **key idea** of this text is _____.	• sleep loss helps explain teenage _____ _____
Q: What are the **most important details** in this text? **A:** (One/Another) **important detail** in this text is _____.	• exhausted adolescents act _____ or make _____ decisions • sleep loss contributes to _____ and _____ problems in school • being sleep-deprived can also make teens feel _____ and more likely to think about committing _____

RESPOND WITH EVIDENCE
Use the frames and evidence from the text to construct a formal written response.

1. What are some trends that are causing adolescents to get inadequate sleep?

   According to the text, one trend that is causing adolescents to get inadequate sleep is

   _____

   This causes teens to get inadequate sleep because _____

   _____

   Another trend that is causing adolescents to get inadequate sleep is _____

   _____

Use the frame to analyze the author's word choice.

2. Use context clues to determine the meaning of "volatile" on page 17.

   "Volatile" means _____

   One context clue that helped me determine the meaning was when Jeremy said his

   emotions were _____

IDENTIFY PRECISE WORDS
Review Text 3 and your *Portfolio* (pp. 38–41) to identify words for your writing.

Topic Words	High-Utility Academic Words
• sleep-deprived	• trend
•	•
•	•

Take a Stand

| Debate | Should school start later to accommodate adolescent sleep needs? |

 COLLABORATE

Read the debate question about teen sleep. Then take turns using a frame to respond with your initial reaction.

Language to RESPOND

So _____, what's your initial reaction?

My initial reaction is _____.

My initial reaction is (similar to/ different from) _____'s.

ANALYZE SOURCES

Read a quote that either supports or opposes the debate question. Then paraphrase.

Quote	Paraphrase
Model: "A study by the National Sleep Foundation (NSF) found that 60 percent of middle and high school students felt tired during the day, and 15 percent had fallen asleep in school in the past year" (Weir 5).	To put it another way, a sleep research organization found that a majority of _____ feel _____ at school, and some claimed to have actually _____ in class.
1. "Lack of sleep can interfere with learning: tired students have a hard time paying attention, and even if they do somehow manage to focus, they may forget what they are taught because memory formation takes place partly during sleep" (Grady 10).	This quote clarifies that sleep-deprived students may have difficulty _____ in class, and may not remember recent lesson _____ because you make _____ when _____
2. "Suburban schools say students behave better, and in the city schools, attendance and graduation rates have gone up and tardiness has decreased" (Grady 13).	This quote clarifies that secondary schools report benefits of _____ including improvements in _____ and _____
3. "The drawback is that some students, especially in city schools, are unable to take part in after-school activities, and some say they are earning less at their after-school jobs" (Grady 13).	This quote clarifies that delaying school start times has _____ on teens' participation in _____ _____ and their wages earned at _____
4. "Many schools, however, have rejected parental pressure to delay school starts, citing bus-cost savings, or the need to keep afternoons open for teens' sports or other activities" (Shellenbarger 18).	To put it another way, a lot of schools simply refuse to shift to a later schedule due to _____ and _____ _____

Debate Ideas

 SYNTHESIZE IDEAS

Write a response to the debate question, including a paraphrase of a text quote and elaboration on the quote.

Claim: My position is that schools (should/should not) _____ start later to accommodate adolescent sleep needs.

Transitional Statement: I have (one key reason/a compelling reason) _____

_____ for taking this stance.

Quote Paraphrase: (According to _____,/The author points out _____.)

_____

_____

_____

Quote Elaboration: (As a result, _____./Consequently, _____.)

_____

_____

_____

 PRESENT EVIDENCE

Maintaining Eye Contact

When presenting ideas during class or in a meeting, maintain **eye contact.** Look at your audience when you speak and make sure to look up from your notes every few seconds so that you look confident and engage your listeners.

LISTEN & TAKE NOTES

Listen attentively and take notes. Then indicate if you agree (+) or disagree (–).

Language to AFFIRM & CLARIFY

That's an interesting opinion. Will you explain _____ again?

Classmate's Name	Idea	+/–

Student Writing Model

Academic Writing Type

A **justification** states a claim and supports it with logical reasons and relevant evidence from texts.

A. The **topic sentence** clearly states the writer's claim about the issue.

B. **Detail sentences** support the claim with reasons and evidence from texts.

C. The **concluding sentence** restates the writer's claim about the issue.

ANALYZE TEXT

Read this student model to analyze the elements of a justification.

A   Evidence from the texts supports the idea that schools should alter start times to accommodate adolescents' sleep needs. One reason is that adolescents would be more alert in school with a later start time. Denise Grady points out in "Sleep Is One Thing Missing in Busy Teenage Lives" that teachers in MN reported that students were less likely to fall asleep in morning classes when they had a one-hour delay in school start time (13). This evidence makes it quite clear that being able to sleep adequately and eat breakfast enables teens to focus instead of nap during early morning

B   classes. An additional reason is that many teens cannot help how sleep-deprived they are in the early morning. In "Understanding the Zombie Teen's Body Clock," Sue Shellenbarger explains how hormones and puberty cause teens' internal clocks to change during adolescence so that they want to stay up later and sleep later (17). This is significant because while younger siblings and parents are becoming tired and preparing to sleep, teens feel wide awake and have trouble settling down. For these reasons, high schools

C   should start later to match teens' sleep patterns.

MARK & DISCUSS ELEMENTS

Mark the justification elements and use the frames to discuss them with your partner.

1. **Circle the writer's claim within the topic sentence.** *The writer's claim is _____.*

2. **Draw a box around four transition words or phrases.**
   One transition (word/phrase) is _____.

3. **Underline and label two reasons that support the writer's claim with the letter R.**
   One reason that supports the writer's claim is _____.

4. **Underline and label two pieces of evidence that support the writer's claim with the letter E.** *One piece of evidence that supports the writer's claim is _____.*

5. **Star four precise topic words and check four high-utility academic words.**
   An example of a (precise topic word/high-utility academic word) is _____.

Transitions to Introduce Evidence

Transitions	Examples
For example,____. *For instance, ____.* *To illustrate, ____.* *As an illustration, ____.* *According to (source), ____.* *The text points out ____.* *In addition, the text states ____.* *In the text, (author's name) explains ____.* *(Author's name) emphasizes ____.*	**For example,** some students in Minnesota say they are more likely to eat breakfast now that they wake up later for school. **According to the National Sleep Foundation,** drivers under 25 cause more than half of the 100,000 traffic crashes due to drowsiness a year. **The text points out** that 15 percent of students say they have fallen asleep in school during the last year. **In the text, Weir explains** that we cycle through the five stages of sleep three to five times a night.

IDENTIFY TRANSITIONS

Review the transitions that writers use to introduce evidence that supports a claim. Then complete each sentence below with an appropriate transition.

1. _____

   that teenagers who are sleep-deprived are more likely to feel depressed.

2. _____

   it is true that many teens are not tired at 9 or 10 p.m.

3. _____

   that many teenagers are resistant to setting bedtimes.

WRITE SUPPORTING EVIDENCE

Write four sentences using transitions to introduce evidence that supports your claim.

1. _____

   _____

   _____

2. _____

   _____

   _____

3. _____

   _____

   _____

4. _____

   _____

   _____

Modal Verbs

Guidelines for Using Modal Verbs

Use **modal verbs** in your justification to describe what is possible or preferable.

The modal verb *should* tells about **something you believe needs to happen.**

> *In my opinion, students **should** finish high school if they want to be successful.*

The modal verb *would* tells about **something you believe is possible in the future.**

> *Higher ticket prices **would** help the drama club raise money.*

The modal verb *could* tells about **something that might be possible in the future.**

> *Students **could** earn more money if the government raised the minimum wage.*

 IDENTIFY MODAL VERBS

Read the justification and circle the modal verbs.

> Evidence from the texts supports the idea that school should not start later to accommodate teen sleep needs. One reason is that adolescents should be trying to keep the same sleep schedule during the week and on weekends. Grady points out in "Sleep Is One Thing Missing in Busy Teenage Lives" that many teens "binge sleep" on the weekends, which leads to more irregular sleep schedules (9). This evidence makes it quite clear that teens could have more regular sleep schedules if they didn't "binge sleep." An additional reason is that many adolescents could take steps to regulate their internal clocks. In "Who Needs Sleep?," Weir explains that viewing bright screens before bedtime can push teens' internal clocks back even further (7). This is significant because if teens stop using bright phones and watching bright TVs in the hour before bed, they would sleep better. For these reasons, schools should not have to change to accommodate adolescents' sleep schedules.

 WRITE MODAL VERBS

Write modal verbs to complete the sentences.

1. Evidence from the texts supports the idea that school _____ start after 9 a.m.

2. Many students _____ feel less irritable if they were able to sleep longer in the mornings.

3. Delaying school start times _____ also reduce the number of teen car accidents due to drowsiness.

4. In addition, many students' grades _____ improve.

5. This option _____ also benefit teachers because students _____ be more alert and focused in class.

Organize a Justification

Prompt	Should school start later to accommodate adolescent sleep needs? Write a justification that states and supports your claim.

IDENTIFY TEXT EVIDENCE

Review the texts to identify evidence that supports each reason.

Reason	Text Evidence
Adolescents who don't get enough sleep might get sick more often.	_____ _____ _____ _____
Schools are concerned that changing start times will affect bus schedules.	_____ _____ _____ _____

PLAN REASONS & EVIDENCE

Use academic language to clearly state your claim as a topic sentence.

Evidence from the texts supports the idea that _____

_____

List two reasons that support your claim and give text evidence for each reason.

Reason 1: _____

_____

_____

Text Evidence: _____

_____

_____

Reason 2: _____

_____

_____

Text Evidence: _____

_____

_____

Restate your claim as a concluding sentence.

For these reasons, _____

_____

Write a Justification

Prompt | Should school start later to accommodate adolescent sleep needs? Write a justification that states and supports your claim.

 WRITE A PARAGRAPH
Use the frame to write your topic sentence, detail sentences, and concluding sentence.

A

Evidence from the texts supports the idea that _____
(claim)

_____

_____

_____

B

One reason is that _____
(1st reason that supports the claim)

_____

_____

_____

_____ points out in _____
(author's name)   (title of source)

_____

that _____
(text evidence)

_____

_____

This evidence makes it quite clear that _____
(elaborate on the evidence)

_____

_____

An additional reason is that _____
(2nd reason that supports the claim)

_____

In _____ , _____
(title of source)   (author's name)

explains that _____
(text evidence)

_____

This is significant because _____
(elaborate on the evidence)

_____

_____

C

For these reasons, _____
(restate your claim)

_____

_____

Rate Your Justification

 ASSESS YOUR DRAFT

Rate your justification. Then have a partner rate it.

Scoring Guide	
1	Insufficient
2	Developing
3	Sufficient
4	Exemplary

1. Does the topic sentence clearly state your claim?	Self	1	2	3	4
	Partner	1	2	3	4
2. Did you include strong reasons to support your claim?	Self	1	2	3	4
	Partner	1	2	3	4
3. Did you provide strong text evidence to support your claim?	Self	1	2	3	4
	Partner	1	2	3	4
4. Did you use transitions to introduce reasons and evidence?	Self	1	2	3	4
	Partner	1	2	3	4
5. Did you include precise topic words and high-utility academic words?	Self	1	2	3	4
	Partner	1	2	3	4
6. Does the concluding sentence restate your claim using new wording?	Self	1	2	3	4
	Partner	1	2	3	4

REFLECT & REVISE

Record specific priorities and suggestions to help you and your partner revise.

(Partner) Positive Feedback: You did an effective job of (organizing/including/stating)

_____

_____

(Partner) Suggestion: Your justification would be stronger if you _____

_____

_____

(Self) Priority 1: I will revise my justification so that it _____

_____

_____

(Self) Priority 2: I also need to _____

_____

_____

CHECK & EDIT

Use this checklist to proofread and edit your justification.

☐ Did you capitalize proper nouns, such as authors' last names?

☐ Did you cite sources using parentheses?

☐ Is each sentence complete?

☐ Are all words spelled correctly?

SHOULD NOT KNOWING ANOTHER LANGUAGE KEEP A DIPLOMA OUT OF REACH?

 BUILD KNOWLEDGE

Read and respond to the Data File (*Issues*, p. 20).

 BRAINSTORM IDEAS

Write a brief list of reasons why students should learn a second language.

- to learn about other countries
- _____
- _____
- _____

 PRESENT IDEAS

Use the frames to discuss ideas with your group. Listen attentively and record the strongest ideas to complete the concept web.

Language to FACILITATE DISCUSSION
So _____, what's your perspective?
_____, what reason did you come up with?

1. Learning another language helps students to _____ (**base verb**: learn)

2. Another reason to learn a second language is to _____ (**base verb**: complete)

3. Students who know a second language may be able to _____ (**base verb**: work)

4. I would like to learn another language so I could _____ (**base verb**: speak)

travel to other countries

REASONS STUDENTS LEARN A SECOND LANGUAGE

Words to Know

BUILD WORD KNOWLEDGE

Rate your word knowledge. Then discuss word meaning and examples with your group.

| ① Don't Know | ② Recognize | ③ Familiar | ④ Know |

Word to Know	Meaning	Examples
1 **admit** *verb* ① ② ③ ④	to let someone _____ a club, school, or group	The honor society only **admits** students who _____ _____
2 **valuable** *adjective* ① ② ③ ④	of great _____	Knowing how to _____ _____ is a **valuable** skill if you want to find a good after-school job.
3 **bilingual** *adjective* ① ② ③ ④	speaking two _____ equally well	The **bilingual** students in our school _____ _____ . _____ _____
4 **competitive** *adjective* ① ② ③ ④	as good as or _____ than others at a job, task, or contest	Our school's _____ is **competitive** with those at other schools because we have _____ _____
1 **culture** *noun* ① ② ③ ④	the way of _____ shared by people in a particular place or society	_____ _____ can be very different from one **culture** to another.
2 **communicate** *verb* ① ② ③ ④	to _____ information or ideas with others	Most teens **communicate** with their friends _____ _____ _____
3 **cognitive** *adjective* ① ② ③ ④	relating to activities of the mind, such as _____ and _____	I use my **cognitive** skills when I _____ _____ _____
4 **linguistic** *adjective* ① ② ③ ④	relating to _____ and _____	The many _____ _____ in our city show its **linguistic** variety.

Academic Discussion

WHAT ARE SOME REASONS WHY STUDENTS PARTICIPATE IN WORLD LANGUAGE CLASSES?

 BRAINSTORM IDEAS

Briefly record at least two ideas in each column using everyday English.

Academic/Career Reasons	Personal Reasons
• graduating from high school • •	• learning about new cultures • •

 ANALYZE WORDS

Complete the chart with precise words to discuss and write about the topic.

Everyday	Precise
job *(noun)*	employment,
talk *(verb)*	communicate,
get *(verb)*	receive,

 MAKE A CLAIM

Rewrite two ideas using the frames and precise words. Then prepare to elaborate verbally.

Language to ELABORATE

For instance, _____.

I have found that _____.

1. **Frame:** One reason why students participate in world language classes is to _____ (**base verb:** learn, fulfill, communicate)

   Response: _____

   _____

2. **Frame:** Based on my experience, students study second languages to _____ (**verb phrase:** graduate from high school, travel to another country, apply to college)

   Response: _____

 COLLABORATE

Listen attentively, restate, and record your partner's ideas.

Language to RESTATE

So your opinion is that _____.

Yes, that's correct.

No, not exactly. What I (stated/reported) was _____.

Classmate's Name	Ideas
	1.
	2.

Ten-Minute Paper

A **ten-minute paper** begins with a well-stated **claim,** followed by **two detail sentences** that elaborate with relevant examples and precise words.

 PRESENT IDEAS

Listen attentively and take notes. Then indicate if you agree (+) or disagree (–).

Classmate's Name	Idea	+/–

ELABORATE IN WRITING

Work with the teacher to write a ten-minute paper.

Language to COLLABORATE

What should we write?

We could put _____. What do you think works well?

We could also write _____.

> One reason why students participate in world language classes is to become more competitive candidates for employment. For example, many companies with offices in foreign countries need _____ employees to _____ with both English and non-English speakers. As a result, an increasing number of English speakers are taking courses that develop their _____ _____ abilities.

Work with a partner to write a ten-minute paper.

> Based on my experience, students study second languages to _____ _____
>
> For example, some of my friends wanted to _____ _____
>
> As a result, they felt it was critical that they be able to _____ _____ in their native language.

Words to Go

 BUILD WORD KNOWLEDGE

Complete the meanings and examples for these high-utility academic words.

Words to Go	Meanings	Examples
benefit ben·e·fit *noun*	something that is _____ or good for you	Being able to _____ _____ is a **benefit** of getting older.
beneficial ben·e·fi·cial *adjective*	having a _____ or _____ effect	_____ _____ can be **beneficial** to a teen's social life.

 DISCUSS & WRITE EXAMPLES

Discuss your response with a partner. Then complete the sentence in writing.

_____ and _____

have **benefits** for football players.

Write your response and read it aloud to a partner.

In my opinion, _____

would be highly _____ for teens' health.

 BUILD WORD KNOWLEDGE

Complete the meanings and examples for these high-utility academic words.

Words to Go	Meanings	Examples
require re·quire *verb*	to _____ something by law or rule	The state **requires** that people _____ _____ to get a driver's license.
requirement re·quire·ment *noun*	something that must be _____ by law or rule	At the restaurant where I work, _____ _____ _____ is a **requirement** for keeping your job.

 DISCUSS & WRITE EXAMPLES

Discuss your response with a partner. Then complete the sentence in writing.

The new school policy **requires** all students to _____

_____

Write your response and read it aloud to a partner.

Maintaining a good attendance record should be a _____ for teens

to _____

Close Reading

BUILD FLUENCY
Read the text "Many Benefits Come With Learning a Foreign Language"
(*Issues*, pp. 21–24).

IDENTIFY KEY IDEAS & DETAILS
Take turns asking and answering questions with a partner. Then write brief notes.

Discussion Frames	Text Notes
Q: What is the **key idea** of this text? A: The **key idea** of this text is _____.	• learning a foreign language has many _____

Q: What are the **most important details** in this text?
 	
A: (One/Another) **important detail** in this text is _____.
	• helps for _____
	
	  and _____
	
	• develops other _____
	  skills
	
	• teaches about other _____

RESPOND WITH EVIDENCE
Use the frames and evidence from the text to construct a formal written response.

1. Based on the text, how is learning a foreign language beneficial?

   According to the author, learning a foreign language is beneficial for a student's

   _____

   In addition, participation in foreign language classes can open up opportunities for

   _____

Use the frame to analyze the author's word choice.

2. Use context clues to determine the meaning of the word *stringent* in the first paragraph on page 22.

   Stringent means _____ One context clue that

   helped me determine the meaning was comparing Stanford's requirement of _____

   _____ with most colleges'

   requirement of _____

IDENTIFY PRECISE WORDS
Review Text 1 and your *Portfolio* (pp. 50–55) to identify words for your writing.

Topic Words	High-Utility Academic Words
• foreign language	• improve
•	•
•	•

Academic Discussion

WHAT ARE THE COGNITIVE AND CULTURAL BENEFITS OF STUDYING A SECOND LANGUAGE?

 BRAINSTORM IDEAS

Briefly record at least two ideas in each column using everyday English.

Cognitive Benefits	Cultural Benefits
• increase vocabulary skills	• reading books in another language
•	•
•	•

 ANALYZE WORDS

Complete the chart with precise words to discuss and write about the issue.

Everyday	Precise
grow *(verb)*	cultivate,
need *(verb)*	entail,
plus *(noun)*	advantage,

 MAKE A CLAIM

Rewrite two ideas using the frames and precise words. Then prepare to elaborate verbally.

> **Language to ELABORATE**
>
> For instance, _____.
>
> I have found that _____.

1. **Frame:** One (cognitive/cultural) benefit of studying a foreign language is _____ (**verb + –ing:** developing skills, scoring well on tests, appreciating others)

   Response: _____

   _____

2. **Frame:** Studying a foreign language is (cognitively/culturally) beneficial because it _____ (**present-tense verb:** enables, allows, requires, increases)

   Response: _____

 COLLABORATE

Listen attentively, restate, and record your partner's ideas.

> **Language to RESTATE**
>
> So your opinion is that _____.
>
> Yes, that's correct.
>
> No, not exactly. What I (stated/reported) was _____.

Classmate's Name	Ideas
	1.
	2.

Ten-Minute Paper

A **ten-minute paper** begins with a well-stated **claim,** followed by **two detail sentences** that elaborate with relevant examples and precise words.

Language to AGREE/DISAGREE
I (agree/disagree) with _____'s opinion.

 PRESENT IDEAS

Listen attentively and take notes. Then write if you agree (+) or disagree (–).

Classmate's Name	Idea	+/–

ELABORATE IN WRITING

Work with the teacher to write a ten-minute paper.

Language to COLLABORATE
What should we write?
We could put _____. What do you think works well?
We could also write _____.

One _____ benefit of studying a foreign language is developing memorization skills that can be an asset in other academic areas. For example, studying Spanish requires that I _____ a great number of _____ One result of this _____ _____ is that when I had to take _____ _____ I found the material _____ to remember.

Work with a partner to write a ten-minute paper.

Studying a foreign language is _____ beneficial because it cultivates relationships with _____ who live in other countries. For example, studying _____ can help someone _____ cousins in _____ One result of _____ _____ is that by the time I left, _____ _____

Words to Go

 BUILD WORD KNOWLEDGE

Complete the meanings and examples for these high-utility academic words.

Words to Go	Meanings	Examples
global glo·bal *adjective*	affecting or involving the whole _____	A global ban on _____ _____ would make _____ _____
globalization glo·bal·i·za·tion *noun*	the process of something becoming present all over the _____	American _____ _____ have become more popular in other countries with the spread of **globalization**.

 DISCUSS & WRITE EXAMPLES

Discuss your response with a partner. Then complete the sentence in writing.

Scientists have studied the effects of **global** warming on _____

_____

Write your response and read it aloud to a partner.

Being able to _____ with a friend on the other

side of the world is one benefit of the _____ of the Internet.

 BUILD WORD KNOWLEDGE

Complete the meaning and examples for this high-utility academic word.

Word to Go	Meaning	Examples
capacity ca·pac·i·ty *noun*	the mental or physical _____ to do or learn something	My brother's **capacity** for _____ is legendary in our family. Having limited **capacity** for _____ _____ I often need _____

 DISCUSS & WRITE EXAMPLES

Discuss your response with a partner. Then complete the sentence in writing.

I firmly believe that girls have the **capacity** to _____

_____

Write your response and read it aloud to a partner.

The fact that teens can _____

proves that their brains have the _____ to do two things at once.

Section Shrink

BUILD FLUENCY

Read the introduction and Section 1 of "The Effects of a Second Language on the Brain" (*Issues*, pp. 25–26).

IDENTIFY KEY IDEAS & DETAILS

Take turns asking and answering questions with a partner. Then write brief notes.

Discussion Frames	Text Notes
Q: What is the **key idea** of this section? A: The **key idea** of this section is _____ .	• bilingualism no longer thought to be harmful
Q: What are the **most important details** in this section? A: (One/Another) **important detail** in this section is _____ . A: Perhaps the **most important detail** in this section is _____ .	• today, being bilingual is a _____ skill, and some countries require foreign language study for _____ • many years ago, believed that bilingualism caused _____ _____ or "split personality" • thought the brain had limited _____ to learn _____

SUMMARIZE

"Shrink" Section 1 of the text by writing a summary in 40 or fewer words.

CLASS SUMMARY   WORD COUNT: _____

Today, becoming _____ is very popular because people value

and often _____ it as an academic and professional

skill, but a century ago, people viewed bilingualism as _____

and _____ for people's brains.

PARTNER SUMMARY   WORD COUNT: _____

Today, people consider _____   _____

because it is a _____ for many colleges

and employers, but long ago people thought it was _____

and beyond the brain's _____

IDENTIFY PRECISE WORDS

Review Section 1 and your *Portfolio* (pp. 56–59) to identify words for your writing.

Topic Words	High-Utility Academic Words
• interconnectivity	• ability
•	•
•	•

Words to Go

 BUILD WORD KNOWLEDGE

Complete the meanings and examples for these high-utility academic words.

Words to Go	Meanings	Examples
invariable in·var·i·a·ble *adjective*	never _____	The **invariable** result of my cooking is _____ _____
invariably in·var·i·a·bly *adverb*	in _____ case; always	Science class is **invariably** so _____ that I _____ _____ every day.

DISCUSS & WRITE EXAMPLES

Discuss your response with a partner. Then complete the sentence in writing.

Every year, a student requests that _____

_____ but the principal's **invariable** response is "No."

Write your response and read it aloud to a partner.

Vandals _____ paint graffiti _____

_____

BUILD WORD KNOWLEDGE

Complete the meanings and examples for these high-utility academic words.

Words to Go	Meanings	Examples
retain re·tain *verb*	to _____ something or continue to have something; to remember	_____ **retains** its _____ if properly cared for.
retention re·ten·tion *noun*	the _____ to keep something in your memory	My mother has a problem with **retention** of _____ _____

DISCUSS & WRITE EXAMPLES

Discuss your response with a partner. Then complete the sentence in writing.

After _____, I **retained** the information that I needed to

_____

Write your response and read it aloud to a partner.

My _____ of facts helps me do well _____

_____

Section Shrink

 BUILD FLUENCY

Read Section 2 of "The Effects of a Second Language on the Brain" (*Issues*, pp. 27–28).

 IDENTIFY KEY IDEAS & DETAILS

Take turns asking and answering questions with a partner.

Discussion Frames	Text Notes
Q: What is the **key idea** of this section? A: The **key idea** of this section is _____.	• learning a _____ has cognitive advantages
Q: What are the **most important details** in this section? A: (One/Another) **important detail** in this section is _____. A: Perhaps the **most important detail** in this section is _____.	• students who _____ a second language had improved English _____ • _____ studying foreign languages had higher verbal and math _____ • _____ children have improved language development

 SUMMARIZE

"Shrink" Section 2 of the text by writing a summary in 40 or fewer words.

CLASS SUMMARY   WORD COUNT: _____

Numerous _____ have discovered that learning a second

language is _____

in that it has been shown to _____ students' test

scores in other academic areas and gives children _____

_____ over their peers.

PARTNER SUMMARY   WORD COUNT: _____

_____ has proven that foreign-language study provides many

_____ such as _____

_____ students' scores on math and English tests and

_____ linguistic abilities.

IDENTIFY PRECISE WORDS

Review Section 2 and your *Portfolio* (pp. 60–61) to identify words for your writing.

Topic Words	High-Utility Academic Words
• monolingual	• distinguish between
•	•
•	•

Words to Go

 BUILD WORD KNOWLEDGE

Complete the meanings and examples for these high-utility academic words.

Words to Go	Meanings	Examples
acquire ac·quire *verb*	to _____ or learn something	I need to practice every day to **acquire** _____ _____
acquisition ac·qui·si·tion *noun*	the process by which someone gains or _____ something	My sister's recent **acquisition** of _____ _____ has caused me to avoid her.

💬 **DISCUSS & WRITE EXAMPLES**

Discuss your response with a partner. Then complete the sentence in writing.

When I read an article about _____ I **acquired** some unsettling

knowledge about _____

Write your response and read it aloud to a partner.

The _____ of _____

is crucial if you want to get a job that _____

 BUILD WORD KNOWLEDGE

Complete the meanings and examples for these high-utility academic words.

Words to Go	Meanings	Examples
impact im·pact *noun*	the _____ of one thing on another	_____ _____ has had a major **impact** on how well I sleep.
impact im·pact *verb*	to have an _____ on someone or something	Other people's opinions will **impact** my decision about which _____

💬 **DISCUSS & WRITE EXAMPLES**

Discuss your response with a partner. Then complete the sentence in writing.

If schools want to have an **impact** on the problem of _____

they need to _____

Write your response and read it aloud to a partner.

The overuse of plastic bags has greatly _____ the _____

_____

Section Shrink

BUILD FLUENCY

Read Section 3 of "The Effects of a Second Language on the Brain" (*Issues*, pp. 28–31).

IDENTIFY KEY IDEAS & DETAILS

Take turns asking and answering questions with a partner.

Discussion Frames	Text Notes
Q: What is the **key idea** of this section? **A:** The **key idea** of this section is _____.	• second languages impact brain _____
Q: What are the **most important details** in this section? **A:** (One/Another) **important detail** in this section is _____. **A:** Perhaps the **most important detail** in this section is _____.	• _____ children and teens have denser _____ _____ • learning a second language at _____ _____ can alter brain _____ • can _____ the onset of Alzheimer's and _____

SUMMARIZE

"Shrink" Section 3 of the text by writing a summary in 40 or fewer words.

CLASS SUMMARY   **WORD COUNT:** _____

Brain _____ have shown that learning a second language

impacts the _____ of brain tissue in young people,

_____ the brain's structure if learned at _____

_____ and helps _____

avoid early onset of Alzheimer's and dementia.

PARTNER SUMMARY   **WORD COUNT:** _____

Scientists have found that _____ a foreign language

_____ the brains of children and teens with _____

_____ gray matter, alters the brain's _____ if

learned early enough, and aids in _____ Alzheimer's and dementia.

IDENTIFY PRECISE WORDS

Review Section 3 and your *Portfolio* (pp. 62–63) to identify words for your writing.

Topic Words	High-Utility Academic Words
• hemisphere	• correlation
•	•
•	•

Student Writing

Academic Writing Type

A **formal written summary** provides an objective overview of the topic and important details from an informational text. The writer credits the author, but writes in primarily his or her own words, without including personal opinions.

> A. The **topic sentence** includes the text type, title, author, and topic.
> B. **Detail sentences** include the important details from the summarized text.
> C. The **concluding sentence** restates the author's conclusion in the writer's own words.

ANALYZE TEXT

Read this student model to analyze the elements of a formal summary.

A

> In the news article titled "Many Benefits Come With Learning a Foreign Language," Kalli Damschen examines the advantages of studying a second language.

B

> First, Damschen explains that a second language can improve students' chances of being admitted to certain colleges. The author also discusses how knowing a foreign language is essential for certain international jobs, and may give a competitive edge for other positions. In addition, she reports that learning another language can improve students' memorization skills. Furthermore, the author describes the cultural benefits, such as learning about other cultures and traveling abroad.

C

> Finally, Damschen concludes that bilingualism presents opportunities for students to be connected to the international community.

MARK & DISCUSS ELEMENTS

Mark the summary elements and use the frames to discuss them with your partner.

1. **Number (1–4) the four elements of the topic sentence.**
   The topic sentence includes the _____.

2. **Draw a box around four transition words or phrases.**
   One transition (word/phrase) is _____.

3. **Underline four important details.** *One important detail in this summary is _____.*

4. **Circle four citation verbs.** *One citation verb that the writer uses is _____.*

5. **Star four precise topic words and check four high-utility academic words.**
   An example of a (precise topic word/high-utility academic word) is _____.

Simple Present-Tense Verbs

Guidelines for Using Simple Present-Tense Verbs

Writers use **simple present-tense verbs** in formal summaries to **cite an author or text.** For singular nouns (*author* or *writer*) and third-person singular pronouns (*he* or *she*), **simple-present tense verbs** end in *-s* or *-es*.

Topic Sentence: State the topic.

Andrianes Pinantoan explores . . .   *The author discusses . . .*   *The article investigates . . .*

Important Details: Summarize details.

He reports . . .   *The writer describes . . .*   *The article explains . . .*

Concluding Sentence: Restate the conclusion.

Pinantoan concludes . . .   *The author sums up . . .*   *Harris ends by . . .*

 IDENTIFY PRESENT-TENSE VERBS

Read the summary below and circle the present-tense verbs that cite the author.

> In the news article titled "Language Immersion Schools Make Strides in St. Louis Area," Jessica Bock explores language immersion schools. First, Bock explains that the latest school to open is a Chinese immersion program. The author also reports that the school teaches all subjects in Chinese, and begins teaching English in the middle of second grade. In addition, she points out that the administrators expect students to score below the state average on standardized tests until they reach fifth grade. Furthermore, the author discusses how students learn a third language in middle school. Finally, Bock concludes that the global business advantages of multilingualism is attracting parents.

 WRITE PRESENT-TENSE VERBS

Complete each sentence with a present-tense citation verb.

1. Kalli Damschen _____ the benefits of studying a second language.

2. Damschen _____ that many colleges require foreign language study.

3. The author _____ that better job opportunities may arise for bilingual people.

4. Finally, Damschen _____ that knowing a second language is quite valuable.

Transitions to Organize Details

Organization	Transitions		Examples
first detail	*First,*	*To begin with,*	**To begin with,** the author reports that second language courses are on the rise.
additional details	*The article also* *In addition,* *Moreover,*	*The author also* *Additionally,* *Furthermore,*	**The author also** points out that bilingual applicants often impress employers. **In addition,** she explains that a second language is often a requirement for getting into college.
last detail	*Finally,*	*Lastly,*	**Finally,** the author concludes that a second language can offer many opportunities.

IDENTIFY TRANSITIONS

Review the transitions that writers use to organize details in a formal summary. Then complete the model summary with appropriate transitions.

_____ the author explains that many foreign language immersion programs are available. _____ discusses how American students live with host families in foreign countries. _____ he describes how the teens are surrounded by people who only speak the foreign language. _____ the author clarifies that the teens also take language courses. _____ the author concludes that immersion programs are highly successful at helping teens become bilingual.

WRITE IMPORTANT DETAILS

Write three sentences about "The Effects of a Second Language on the Brain" using transitions.

1. _____   _____
   (Transition)   (noun/pronoun)
   _____ that _____
   (citation verb)   (important detail)
   _____
   _____

2. _____   _____
   (Transition)   (noun/pronoun)
   _____ that _____
   (citation verb)   (important detail)
   _____
   _____

3. _____   _____
   (Transition)   (noun/pronoun)
   _____ that _____
   (citation verb)   (important detail)
   _____

Organize a Formal Summary

Prompt Write a formal summary of "The Effects of a Second Language on the Brain."

Guidelines for Paraphrasing Multiple Sentences
Paraphrase related details from a source text by combining key information into one sentence. Replace key words and phrases with synonyms and keep important topic words.

Text Detail 1	Text Detail 2	Text Detail 3
"…babies from bilingual homes were able to distinguish between different languages, while those from monolingual homes could not" (Pinantoan 9).	"…students who studied a foreign language invariably did better on the English portion of the Louisiana Basic Skill tests than those who did not" (Pinantoan 11).	"While those who did not study foreign language had a mean of 366 on the verbal SAT and 409 on the math SAT, those with…five years of foreign language scored dramatically higher (504 and 535)" (Pinantoan 13).

PARAPHRASE IDEAS
Combine key information from the three text details above into one detail sentence.

Bilingual babies, children, and teens have outperformed their monolingual peers with

(Text Detail 1) _____

(Text Detail 2) _____ and

(Text Detail 3) _____

PLAN KEY IDEAS & DETAILS
State the text information to write a topic sentence.

In the blog post titled (title) _____

(author's full name) _____ (citation verb: explores, examines, discusses)

_____ (topic) _____

List four important details from the article primarily using your own words.

1. _____

_____

2. _____

_____

3. _____

_____

4. _____

_____

Restate the author's conclusion in your own words.

_____

_____

Write a Formal Summary

Prompt | Write a formal summary of "The Effects of a Second Language on the Brain."

✎ WRITE A PARAGRAPH

Use the frame to write your topic sentence, detail sentences, and concluding sentence.

A

In the blog post titled _____
(title)

_____

_____ _____
(author's full name)   (citation verb)

_____
(topic)

B

_____ _____ _____
(Transition)   (author's last name)   (citation verb)

_____
(1st important detail)

_____

The (author/writer) _____ also _____
(citation verb)

_____
(2nd important detail)

_____

_____ (he/she) _____ _____
(Transition)   (citation verb)

_____
(3rd important detail)

_____

_____ the (author/writer) _____
(Transition)

_____ _____
(citation verb)   (4th important detail)

_____

_____

C

_____ _____ concludes that
(Transition)   (author's last name)

_____
(restate author's conclusion)

_____

_____

Rate Your Summary

 ASSESS YOUR DRAFT
Rate your formal summary. Then have a partner rate it.

Scoring Guide	
1	Insufficient
2	Developing
3	Sufficient
4	Exemplary

1. Does the topic sentence state the title, author, and topic?	Self	1	2	3	4
	Partner	1	2	3	4
2. Did you paraphrase the most important details from the text?	Self	1	2	3	4
	Partner	1	2	3	4
3. Did you use citation verbs to credit the author?	Self	1	2	3	4
	Partner	1	2	3	4
4. Did you use transitions to introduce and sequence details?	Self	1	2	3	4
	Partner	1	2	3	4
5. Did you include precise topic words and high-utility academic words?	Self	1	2	3	4
	Partner	1	2	3	4
6. Did you restate the author's conclusion using your own words?	Self	1	2	3	4
	Partner	1	2	3	4

REFLECT & REVISE
Record specific priorities and suggestions to help you and your partner revise.

(Partner) Positive Feedback: I appreciate how you (used/included) _____

_____

_____

(Partner) Suggestion: As you revise your summary, focus on _____

_____

_____

(Self) Priority 1: My summary paragraph needs _____

_____

_____

(Self) Priority 2: I plan to improve my summary by _____

_____

_____

CHECK & EDIT
Use this checklist to proofread and edit your formal summary.

☐ Did you capitalize the title of the article and proper nouns?

☐ Did you put quotation marks around the title of the article?

☐ Do simple present-tense verbs end in –s?

☐ Is each sentence complete?

☐ Are all words spelled correctly?

Words to Know

 BUILD WORD KNOWLEDGE

Rate your word knowledge. Then discuss word meanings and examples with your group.

		① Don't Know	② Recognize	③ Familiar	④ Know

Word to Know	Meaning	Examples
1 **conflict** *noun* ① ② ③ ④	a situation in which people do not _____	_____ _____ can cause **conflicts** between friends. I had a **conflict** with my parents about _____ _____ _____
2 **generation** *noun* ① ② ③ ④	all the people who are about the same _____	My **generation** is known for communicating by _____ _____ _____ Families often pass down _____ _____ _____ from **generation** to **generation**.
3 **identity** *noun* ① ② ③ ④	a sense of _____; a feeling of _____ to a particular group or race	An important part of my **identity** is my _____ _____ Teens sometimes shape their **identities** by _____ _____
4 **primary language** *noun* ① ② ③ ④	the language that someone uses most _____	My family's **primary language** is _____ If immigrants want English to become their **primary language**, they should _____ _____ _____ _____

Close Reading

 READ THE TEXT

Read the poem "Bilingual/Bilingüe" (*Issues*, pp. 32–33).

 IDENTIFY STRUCTURE

Poetry's Structure

The **structure** of a poem is how it is organized. A **couplet** is two lines of poetry that usually rhyme. A poem's **rhyme scheme** is the pattern it uses for words that rhyme. To identify a rhyme scheme, write *A* at the end of the first line and then write *A* at the end of any lines that end with a rhyming word. Write *B* at the end of the next line that does not rhyme, and so on.

Use the frames to analyze the poem's structure.

1. What is the structure of the poem "Bilingual/Bilingüe"?

   The poem "Bilingual/Bilingüe" contains _____ couplets, each of

   which consists of _____

2. What is the rhyme scheme of the poem "Bilingual/Bilingüe"?

   The rhyme scheme of the poem "Bilingual/Bilingüe" is that _____

   _____

   For example, the words _____ and _____ rhyme.

 ANALYZE CRAFT & STRUCTURE

Use the frames to analyze the author's use of language.

3. What is the effect of including Spanish words in the poem?

   One effect of including Spanish words in the poem is to show _____

   _____

   _____

   Most of the Spanish words are surrounded by _____

   which separate them from the English words. However, in the last couplet, the author

   says _____

   which shows that _____

   _____

 ANALYZE THEME

Use the frames to analyze the poem's theme.

4. How does "and still the heart was one" contribute to the poem's theme, or overall message?

   The phrase "and still the heart was one" means that Espaillat remained _____

   _____

   She wants the reader to understand that _____

   _____

Academic Discussion
HOW DOES LANGUAGE INFLUENCE OUR IDENTITY?

 BRAINSTORM IDEAS

Briefly record at least two ideas in each column using everyday English.

Individual Effects	Community Effects
• what someone is able to read	• references to music, TV shows, and movies
•	•
•	•

 ANALYZE WORDS

Complete the chart with precise words to discuss and write about the topic.

Everyday	Precise
decide *(verb)*	determine,
difference of opinion *(noun)*	disagreement,
group of people *(noun)*	peers,

 MAKE A CLAIM

Rewrite two ideas using the frames and precise words. Then prepare to elaborate verbally.

1. **Frame:** Language influences our identity because it _____ (**present-tense verb:** allows, affects, determines)

   Response: _____

   _____

2. **Frame:** Rhina P. Espaillat shows that language influences her identity by _____ (**verb + –ing:** saying, writing, showing)

   Response: _____

> **Language to ELABORATE**
> For instance, _____.
> I have found that _____.

 COLLABORATE

Listen attentively, restate, and record your partner's ideas.

Classmate's Name	Ideas
	1.
	2.

> **Language to RESTATE**
> So your opinion is that _____.
> Yes, that's correct.
> No, not exactly. What I (stated/reported) was _____.

Ten-Minute Paper

A **ten-minute paper** begins with a well-stated **claim,** followed by **two detail sentences** that elaborate with relevant examples and precise words.

Language to AGREE/DISAGREE

I (agree/disagree) with _____'s opinion.

 PRESENT IDEAS

Listen attentively and take notes. Then write if you agree (+) or disagree (–).

Classmate's Name	Idea	+/–

ELABORATE IN WRITING

Work with the teacher to write a ten-minute paper.

Language to COLLABORATE

What should we write?

We could put _____. What do you think works well?

We could also write _____.

Language influences our identity because it determines which people are in our social circle. For example, Spanish speakers often shop at stores where _____ _____ speak the same _____

As a result, people who speak the same language often live _____ _____ and form _____

Rhina P. Espaillat explores this in her poem "Bilingual/Bilingüe" when she writes that keeping English and Spanish separate could _____ _____

Work with a partner to write a ten-minute paper.

Language influences our identity because it influences _____ _____ For example, when people immigrate to the United States, their children often _____

As a result, different language abilities in a family can cause _____ _____

Rhina P. Espaillat explores this in her poem "Bilingual/Bilingüe" when she discusses _____ _____

Take a Stand

Debate | Should studying a second language be a graduation requirement?

 COLLABORATE

Read the debate question about second languages. Then take turns using a frame to respond with your initial reaction.

Language to RESPOND

So _____, what's your initial reaction?

My initial reaction is _____.

My initial reaction is (similar to/ different from) _____'s.

ANALYZE SOURCES

Read a quote that either supports or opposes the debate topic. Then paraphrase.

Quote	Paraphrase
Model: "Foreign language classes foster abilities such as memorization and critical thinking that can improve academic performance in other subjects" (Damschen 23).	In other words, _____ a second language can benefit students in other classes because it helps them _____ and _____
1. "25% of four-year universities require students to have studied a language other than English in high school. 51% of four-year universities require students to study a foreign language to earn a degree" (Modern Language Association 20).	In other words, three out of four _____ do not require language study for _____ and almost half do not require it for _____
2. "Prestigious schools often have more stringent requirements. Stanford, for example, requires three or more years of a foreign language. Princeton expects four, while only requiring two years of both history and science" (Damschen 22).	This quote clarifies that the best universities _____ students to _____ while in _____
3. "Bryan Andrews, a senior studying French at Northridge, says, 'It's really hard because there are so many different verbs you have to learn. You have to have a lot of memorization skills and learn a lot of new concepts'" (Damschen 23).	In other words, to _____ a second language, students must be able to _____ a lot of material, which may be very _____
4 "Bilingualism can very well translate to better job opportunities and better pay. In some career paths, fluency in more than one language is an absolute requirement" (Pinantoan 25).	This quote clarifies that becoming _____ in a second language can _____ students by helping them obtain _____

Debate Ideas

 SYNTHESIZE IDEAS

Write a response to the debate question, including a paraphrase of a text quote and elaboration on the quote.

Claim: My position is that a second language (should/should not) _____ be a graduation requirement.

Transitional Statement: I have (one key reason/a compelling reason) _____

_____ for taking this stance.

Quote Paraphrase: (According to _____,/The author points out _____.)

_____

_____

_____

Quote Elaboration: (As a result, _____./Consequently, _____.)

_____

_____

 PRESENT EVIDENCE

Using a Public Voice

When presenting ideas during class or in a meeting, use your **public voice.** Speak two times slower and three times louder than when you interact socially to make sure your audience grasps your key points.

LISTEN & TAKE NOTES

Listen attentively and take notes. Then indicate if you agree (+) or disagree (–).

> **Language to AFFIRM & CLARIFY**
>
> That's an interesting claim.
> I have a question about _____.

Classmate's Name	Idea	+/–

Student Writing Model

Academic Writing Type

A **justification** states a claim and supports it with logical reasons and relevant evidence from texts.

> A. The **topic sentence** clearly states the writer's claim about the issue.
> B. **Detail sentences** support the claim with reasons and evidence from texts.
> C. The **concluding sentence** restates the writer's claim about the issue.

ANALYZE TEXT

Read this student model to analyze the elements of a justification.

A
Evidence from the texts supports the position that a second language should not be a requirement for graduation. One reason is that retaining the information necessary to learn a second language is difficult for some students. Kalli Damschen points out in "Many Benefits Come With Learning a Foreign Language" that Bryan Andrews struggled to learn French verbs (23). This evidence makes it quite clear that students with less developed linguistic skills may risk losing

B
valuable points from their GPAs. An additional reason is that such a strict requirement is unnecessary. According to the Modern Language Association, only one-quarter of four-year colleges require applicants to have studied a second language. This is significant because most universities do not require language study and pursuing other interests can make applicants competitive. For these reasons, schools should not

C
require students to study a foreign language to earn a diploma.

MARK & DISCUSS ELEMENTS

Mark the justification elements and use the frames to discuss them with your partner.

1. **Circle the writer's claim within the topic sentence.** *The writer's claim is _____.*

2. **Draw a box around four transition words or phrases.**
   One transition (word/phrase) is _____.

3. **Underline and label two reasons that support the writer's claim with the letter *R*.**
   One reason that supports the writer's claim is _____.

4. **Underline and label two pieces of evidence that support the writer's claim with the letter *E*.** *One piece of evidence that supports the writer's claim is _____.*

5. **Star four precise topic words and check four high-utility academic words.**
   An example of a (precise topic word/high-utility academic word) is _____.

Paraphrasing Text

Guidelines for Paraphrasing a Sentence

Paraphrase one sentence from a source text by keeping important topic words and replacing key words and phrases with synonyms.

Source Text	Key Words & Phrases → Synonyms		Paraphrasing
"There are hundreds of thousands of people who don't know English, making the ability to speak and write a different language a valuable commodity in many careers" (Damschen 22).	hundreds of thousands	→ countless	Countless people cannot communicate in English, so being bilingual is a highly beneficial skill to have in numerous careers.
	don't know	→ cannot communicate in	
	ability to speak and and write a different language	→ being bilingual	
	valuable commodity	→ highly beneficial skill	
	many	→ numerous	

IDENTIFY PRECISE SYNONYMS

Read these statements and replace the words in parentheses with synonyms.

1. Studying a foreign language is (a requirement) _____ in some schools in the United States.

2. (The ability to speak a foreign language) _____ can be very helpful in any job that deals with people, particularly in careers that have (an international) _____ focus.

3. In fact, various (experiments) _____ since then have shown that the study of foreign languages is linked to various (cognitive advantages.) _____ _____

PARAPHRASE IDEAS

Paraphrase the three statements above using primarily your own words.

1. Pinantoan points out that _____

_____

_____

2. According to "Many Benefits Come With Learning a Foreign Language," _____

_____

_____

3. Pinantoan also explains that _____

_____

Regular Past-Tense Verbs

Guidelines for Using Regular Past-Tense Verbs

A **regular past-tense verb** tells about an action that already happened. Regular past-tense verbs end in *–ed*.

Use regular past-tense verbs in your justification to describe relevant evidence from your experience.

> I **watched** *a documentary that* **explained** *the benefits of studying foreign languages.*
>
> I **completed** *the language course with a barely passing grade.*
>
> *My brother* **studied** *two languages in high school and three colleges* **admitted** *him.*

 IDENTIFY PAST-TENSE VERBS

Read the justification and circle the regular past-tense verbs.

> Evidence from the texts supports the claim that schools should make learning a second language a requirement to graduate. One reason is that it would improve graduates' job opportunities. Andrianes Pinantoan points out in "The Effects of a Second Language on the Brain" that some careers require bilingualism (25). For example, my sister was not qualified for some positions because she never studied Spanish, so the employers hired other candidates. An additional reason is that speaking another language allows teens to fully engage with people from other parts of the world. According to Kalli Damschen's article "Many Benefits Come With Learning a Foreign Language," knowing another language helps people understand other cultures (24). In my own experience, when I visited Mexico after learning Spanish, I experienced the culture and the people in a different way. For these reasons, foreign language study should be required for graduating from high school.

 WRITE PAST-TENSE VERBS

Complete the sentences with the past tense of the regular verbs in parentheses.

1. Last year, I _____ to learn Arabic because I want to have an international job someday. (try)

2. At first, I found the classes extremely difficult and I _____ that I would never learn the language. (believe)

3. However, soon I _____ almost everything. (comprehend)

4. By the end of the course, I _____ that I could even make jokes in Arabic. (realize)

5. Last week, I _____ to find out about an internship at a company with offices in Qatar. (call)

Organize a Justification

Prompt	Should studying a second language be a graduation requirement? Write a justification that states and supports your claim.

IDENTIFY TEXT EVIDENCE

Review the texts to identify evidence that supports each reason.

Reason	Text Evidence
Students should have time to pursue other subjects, such as technology and the arts.	
Second languages can make teens better equipped to work in a global economy.	

PLAN REASONS & EVIDENCE

Use academic language to clearly state your claim as a topic sentence.

Evidence from the texts supports the idea that _____

_____

List two reasons that support your claim and give text evidence for each reason.

Reason 1: _____

_____

_____

Evidence: _____

_____

_____

Reason 2: _____

_____

_____

Evidence: _____

_____

_____

Restate your claim as a concluding sentence.

For these reasons, _____

_____

Write a Justification

Prompt | Should studying a second language be a graduation requirement? Write a justification that states and supports your claim.

✏️ WRITE A PARAGRAPH
Use the frame to write your topic sentence, detail sentences, and concluding sentence.

A

Evidence from the texts supports the (idea/position/premise)

_____ that _____
(claim)

_____

_____

B

One reason is that _____
(1st reason that supports the claim)

_____

_____

_____

_____ points out in _____
(Author)   (title of source)

_____

that _____
(text evidence)

_____

This (evidence/data) _____ makes it quite clear that

_____
(elaborate on evidence)

An additional reason is that _____
(2nd reason that supports the claim)

_____

_____

According to _____
(source)

_____

_____
(text evidence)

_____

This is significant because _____
(elaborate on the evidence)

_____

C

For these reasons, _____
(restate the claim)

_____

_____

Rate Your Justification

Scoring Guide	
1	Insufficient
2	Developing
3	Sufficient
4	Exemplary

 ASSESS YOUR DRAFT

Rate your justification. Then have a partner rate it.

1. Does the topic sentence clearly state your claim?	Self	1	2	3	4
	Partner	1	2	3	4
2. Did you include strong reasons to support your claim?	Self	1	2	3	4
	Partner	1	2	3	4
3. Did you provide strong text evidence to support your claim?	Self	1	2	3	4
	Partner	1	2	3	4
4. Did you use transitions to introduce reasons and evidence?	Self	1	2	3	4
	Partner	1	2	3	4
5. Did you include precise topic words and high-utility academic words?	Self	1	2	3	4
	Partner	1	2	3	4
6. Does the concluding sentence restate your claim using new wording?	Self	1	2	3	4
	Partner	1	2	3	4

REFLECT & REVISE

Record specific priorities and suggestions to help you and your partner revise.

(Partner) Positive Feedback: You did an effective job of (organizing/including/stating)

_____

_____

(Partner) Suggestion: Your justification would be stronger if you _____

_____

_____

(Self) Priority 1: I will revise my justification so that it _____

_____

_____

(Self) Priority 2: I also need to _____

_____

_____

CHECK & EDIT

Use this checklist to proofread and edit your justification.

☐ Did you capitalize proper nouns, such as authors' names?

☐ Did you cite sources using parentheses?

☐ Is each sentence complete?

☐ Are all words spelled correctly?

60-Second Speech

IDENTIFY TOPIC
Choose one of the questions below to address in a 60-second speech.

☐ Should our school change its start time?

☐ Should our school make any changes to its world language program?

BRAINSTORM IDEAS
Write your claim and two reasons that support it.

My Claim: _____

Reason 1: _____

Reason 2: _____

SYNTHESIZE IDEAS
Take notes on supporting evidence and a counterclaim.

Evidence 1: _____

_____

Evidence 2: _____

_____

Counterclaim: _____

_____

Response: _____

_____

WRITE A SPEECH
Write a 60-second speech that states your claim and includes reasons, evidence, and a counterclaim.

I believe that _____

_____

One reason I maintain this position is that _____

_____

Secondly, _____

_____

To illustrate, _____

_____

The opposition might claim that _____

_____

However, _____

_____

For these reasons, I _____ that _____

_____

Present & Rate Your Speech

Using a Public Voice
When presenting ideas during class or in a meeting, use your **public voice.** Speak two times slower and three times louder than when you interact socially to make sure your audience grasps your key points.

PRESENT YOUR SPEECH
Present your speech to the small group. Make sure to use a public voice.

LISTEN & TAKE NOTES
Listen attentively and take notes. Then indicate if you agree (+) or disagree (–).

Language to AFFIRM & CLARIFY

That's an interesting claim.
I have a question about _____.

Classmate's Name	Idea	+/–

ASSESS YOUR SPEECH
Use the Scoring Guide to rate your speech.

Scoring Guide			
1	Insufficient	3	Sufficient
2	Developing	4	Exemplary

	1	2	3	4
1. Did your topic sentence clearly state your claim?	1	2	3	4
2. Did you include strong reasons and evidence to support your speech?	1	2	3	4
3. Did you include precise topic words?	1	2	3	4
4. Were you easy to understand?	1	2	3	4
5. Did you use a public voice?	1	2	3	4

REFLECT
Write two ways you can improve for your next speech.

Priority 1: I can improve my next speech by _____

_____

_____

Priority 2: When I present my next speech, I will focus on _____

_____

_____

Are teens old enough to get behind the wheel?

BUILD KNOWLEDGE
Read and respond to the Data File (*Issues*, p. 34).

BRAINSTORM IDEAS
Write a brief list of the pros and cons of allowing teens to drive.

- pro: get around on their own
- _____
- _____
- _____

PRESENT IDEAS
Use the frames to discuss ideas with your group. Listen attentively and record the strongest ideas to complete the T-chart.

- I know teen drivers who _____ (**present-tense verb:** give)
- Allowing teens to drive means they (may/may not) _____ (**base verb: help**)
- Teen drivers might also _____ (**base verb:** enjoy)
- Additionally, some teen drivers like to _____ (**base verb:** talk)

Language to FACILITATE DISCUSSION

So _____, what's your perspective?

_____, what example did you come up with?

PROS	CONS
• get around on their own	• fill car with too many people
•	•
•	•
•	•

Words to Know

 BUILD WORD KNOWLEDGE

Rate your word knowledge. Then discuss word meanings and examples with your group.

	① Don't Know	② Recognize	③ Familiar	④ Know

Word to Know	Meaning	Examples
1 distraction *noun* ① ② ③ ④	something that takes your _____ away from what you are doing	In order to avoid **distractions**, I usually do my homework _____ _____
2 experienced *adjective* ① ② ③ ④	having _____ _____ because you have done something for a long time	After years of _____ I have become an **experienced** _____
3 risk *noun* ① ② ③ ④	the chance that something _____ may happen; something likely to cause _____ _____	I never _____ because the risk of _____ _____ is too great.
4 ban *verb* ① ② ③ ④	to not _____ something to be done, seen, or used	Our principal wants to **ban** students from _____ _____ because it leads to _____
1 impulsive *adjective* ① ② ③ ④	acting _____ thinking about the possible results or dangers	I have plans for my future, so I would never be so **impulsive** as to _____ _____
2 supervision *noun* ① ② ③ ④	the act of watching over an activity or person to make sure things are done _____	My little brother needs a lot of **supervision**, so my parents often _____ _____
3 impose *verb* ① ② ③ ④	to _____ people to accept a rule, punishment, or tax	After I _____ my parents **imposed** a rule that I had to _____ _____
4 inconvenience *noun* ① ② ③ ④	_____ caused by someone or something which affect or annoy you	_____ _____ may seem like an **inconvenience**, but it is a responsible thing to do.

Academic Discussion
What are some distractions that prevent drivers from being safe?

 BRAINSTORM IDEAS

Briefly record at least two ideas in each column using everyday English.

Technology	Activities
• checking GPS	• eating or snacking
•	•
•	•

 ANALYZE WORDS

Complete the chart with precise words to discuss and write about the topic.

Everyday	Precise
answer *(verb)*	reply,
look *(verb)*	examine,
many *(adjective)*	abundance,

 MAKE A CLAIM

Rewrite two ideas using the frames and precise words. Then prepare to elaborate verbally.

> **Language to ELABORATE**
>
> In particular, _____.
>
> I have noticed that _____.

1. **Frame:** One distraction that prevents drivers from being safe is _____ (**verb + –ing**: texting friends, listening to music, putting on makeup)

   Response: _____

   _____

2. **Frame:** Based on my experience, _____ (**noun phrase**: incoming text messages, phone calls, loud passengers) may distract drivers and prevent them from being safe.

   Response: _____

   _____

 COLLABORATE

Listen attentively, restate, and record your partner's ideas.

> **Language to RESTATE**
>
> So your perspective is that _____.
>
> Yes, that's correct.
>
> No, not quite. What I (reported/expressed) is that _____.

Classmate's Name	Ideas
	1.
	2.

Ten-Minute Paper

A **ten-minute paper** begins with a well-stated **claim** followed by **two detail sentences** that elaborate with relevant examples and precise words.

PRESENT IDEAS

Listen attentively and take notes. Then indicate if you agree (+) or disagree (–).

Classmate's Name	Idea	+/–

ELABORATE IN WRITING

Work with the teacher to write a ten-minute paper.

One distraction that prevents drivers from being safe is having a serious or intense discussion with a passenger. For example, at a particularly sensitive point in the conversation, the driver may have the _____ to glance at the passenger. As a result, the driver _____ not _____ what is happening on the road.

Work with a partner to write a ten-minute paper.

One distraction that prevents drivers from being safe is responding to _____ _____ For example, in order to _____ to a _____ the driver not only has to _____ but also has to _____ As a result, the driver's eyes are not _____ and he or she has only one hand _____ _____

Words to Go

 BUILD WORD KNOWLEDGE

Complete the meanings and examples for these high-utility academic words.

Words to Go	Meanings	Examples
restriction re·stric·tion *noun*	a rule or law that _____ what you can do or what can happen	My parents put a **restriction** on _____ _____ _____
restricted re·strict·ed *adjective*	limited or _____	Most students have **restricted** access to _____ at school.

 DISCUSS & WRITE EXAMPLES

Discuss your response with a partner. Then complete the sentence in writing.

Most amusement park rides have **restrictions**, limiting _____

_____ and requiring _____

Write your response and read it aloud to a partner.

The sidewalk outside our apartment has a _____ amount of space,

so we go to the park when we want to _____

 BUILD WORD KNOWLEDGE

Complete the meaning and examples for this high-utility academic word.

Word to Go	Meaning	Examples
alternative al·ter·na·tive *noun*	something you can choose _____ _____ something else	As an **alternative** to _____ _____ I chose to _____ If you want to have a snack, a healthy **alternative** is _____ _____

 DISCUSS & WRITE EXAMPLES

Discuss your response with a partner. Then complete the sentence in writing.

As an **alternative** to watching TV, sometimes I _____

_____

Write your response and read it aloud to a partner.

Reusable and biodegradable bags are good _____ to using

_____

Close Reading

 BUILD FLUENCY

Read the text "DN'T TXT N DRV" (*Issues*, pp. 35–38).

 IDENTIFY KEY IDEAS & DETAILS

Take turns asking and answering questions with a partner. Then write brief notes.

Discussion Frames	Text Notes
Q: What is the author's **main idea**? **A:** The author's **main idea** is _____.	• texting and driving _____ not worth the _____

Q: What are the **key details** in this text?
 	
A: (One/Another) **key detail** in this text
  is _____.
	• distracted driving causes high
	
	  _____ of crashes
	
	• many states _____
	
	  cell phones and driving
	
	• teens _____ taking
	
	  steps to _____ accidents

 RESPOND WITH EVIDENCE

Use the frame and evidence from the text to construct a formal written response.

1. According to the author, how does texting compare to other driver distractions?

   According to the author, texting is _____

   than _____ because

   _____ while texting.

Use the frame to analyze the structure the author uses to organize the text.

2. What is the effect of the bulleted text in the section "Why Cells and Driving Don't Mix"?

   The bulleted text in the section "Why Cells and Driving Don't Mix" has the effect of

   _____

   _____

   The bulleted text accomplishes this effect because it includes _____

   _____

IDENTIFY PRECISE WORDS

Review Text 1 and your *Portfolio* (pp. 84–89) to identify words for your writing.

Topic Words	High-Utility Academic Words
• fatal accidents	• concentrate
•	•
•	•

Academic Discussion
What is an alternative to distracted driving?

 BRAINSTORM IDEAS

Briefly record at least two ideas in each column using everyday English.

Drivers	Passengers
• use talking GPS	• don't argue with driver
•	•
•	•

 ANALYZE WORDS

Complete the chart with precise words to discuss and write about the issue.

Everyday	Precise
pay attention *(verb)*	focus,
careless *(adjective)*	distracted,
ask *(verb)*	solicit,

MAKE A CLAIM

Rewrite two ideas using the frames and precise words. Then prepare to elaborate verbally.

Language to ELABORATE
In particular, _____.
I have noticed that _____.

1. **Frame:** An alternative to _____ (**verb** + *–ing:* texting, eating, arguing) while driving is _____ (**verb** + *–ing:* turning off your cell phone, eating before leaving home, waiting until you arrive)

   Response: _____

   _____

2. **Frame:** As an alternative to _____ (**verb** + *–ing:* texting, making calls, searching for), drivers can _____ (**verb phrase:** ask a passenger, pull over to the side)

   Response: _____

   _____

 COLLABORATE

Listen attentively, restate, and record your partner's ideas.

Classmate's Name	Ideas
	1.
	2.

Language to RESTATE
So your perspective is that _____.
Yes, that's correct.
No, not quite. What I (reported/expressed) was _____.

Ten-Minute Paper

A **ten-minute paper** begins with a well-stated **claim** followed by **two detail sentences** that elaborate with relevant examples and precise words.

PRESENT IDEAS

Listen attentively and take notes. Then indicate if you agree (+) or disagree (–).

Classmate's Name	Idea	+/–

ELABORATE IN WRITING

Work with the teacher to write a ten-minute paper.

An alternative to eating while driving is stopping at a restaurant to have a meal. For example, eating while driving _____ requires the driver to _____ on the food and not making a mess, instead of _____ on the road. As a result, the driver may be too _____ to notice potential _____

Work with a partner to write a ten-minute paper.

As an alternative to placing a phone call while driving, drivers can _____
_____
For example, if you need to call _____
to inform them _____
you can hand the phone to _____ and request that
_____
As a result, your important _____
will still be delivered, and you will have reduced the risk of _____
_____

Words to Go

 BUILD WORD KNOWLEDGE

Complete the meanings and examples for these high-utility academic words.

Words to Go	Meanings	Examples
mature ma·ture *adjective*	fully _____ or _____ ; to act _____ than your age	My brother's body is **mature**, which puts him at an advantage when _____ _____
immature im·ma·ture *adjective*	_____ grown or developed; to act _____ than your age	I'm only a freshman, so my plans for _____ _____ are still **immature**.

 DISCUSS & WRITE EXAMPLES

Discuss your response with a partner. Then complete the sentence in writing.

My little cousin made a **mature** decision when she chose to save her money instead of

_____

Write your response and read it aloud to a partner.

Even though my older brother is intelligent, he often makes _____

jokes when _____

 BUILD WORD KNOWLEDGE

Complete the meaning and examples for this high-utility academic word.

Word to Go	Meaning	Examples
conduct con·duct *verb*	to _____ an activity or process, especially to get _____ or prove facts	As a reporter for the school paper, I got to **conduct** an interview with _____ _____ The student council **conducted** a survey on _____

DISCUSS & WRITE EXAMPLES

Discuss your response with a partner. Then complete the sentence in writing.

I strongly contend that scientists should not **conduct** experiments that _____

_____

Write your response and read it aloud to a partner.

Last year, my friends and I _____ a poll to find out _____

_____

Section Shrink

 BUILD FLUENCY
Read the introduction and Section 1 of "Is 16 Too Young to Drive a Car?"
(*Issues*, pp. 39–42).

 IDENTIFY KEY IDEAS & DETAILS
Take turns asking and answering questions with a partner. Then write brief notes.

Discussion Frames	Text Notes
Q: What is this section **mainly about**? **A:** This section is **mainly about** _____.	• 16-year-old drivers are considered _____
Q: What are the **key details** in this section? **A:** (One/Another) **key detail** in this section is _____. **A:** Perhaps the **most important key detail** in this section is _____.	• part of brain that weighs risks, makes judgments, and controls impulses is _____ in teens • most American adults favor raising the _____ ; so far only _____ imposed • 16-year-olds involved in five times more fatal _____

 SUMMARIZE

"Shrink" Section 1 of the text by writing a summary in 40 or fewer words.

CLASS SUMMARY: **WORD COUNT:** _____

Studies show that a critical part of 16-year-olds' brains is _____

explaining why teens cause more fatal accidents than _____

_____ and justifying driving _____

and the majority opinion that _____

PARTNER SUMMARY: **WORD COUNT:** _____

Studies prove that the brains of 16-year-olds are _____

clarifying why teen drivers cause _____ than

older drivers, and warranting enforced _____ and the claim of most

Americans that teens should be older before they _____

IDENTIFY PRECISE WORDS
Review Section 1 and your *Portfolio* (pp. 90–93) to identify words for your writing.

Topic Words	High-Utility Academic Words
• impulsive behavior	• vital
•	•
•	•

Words to Go

 BUILD WORD KNOWLEDGE
Complete the meaning and examples for this high-utility academic word.

Word to Go	Meaning	Examples
involve in·volve *verb*	to be a _____ or a result of an activity or situation; to _____ something	I was _____ when I learned that my science class **involved** _____ Preparing for our high school play **involved** _____

 DISCUSS & WRITE EXAMPLES
Discuss your response with a partner. Then complete the sentence in writing.

Our school's day of community service **involved** _____

_____

Write your response and read it aloud to a partner.

When my parents decided to get a dog, my sister and I were _____

in _____

BUILD WORD KNOWLEDGE
Complete the meaning and examples for this high-utility academic word.

Word to Go	Meaning	Examples
acknowledge ac·know·ledge *verb*	to _____ _____ the truth about something	After I lost my keys again, I had to **acknowledge** that _____ My competitive sister finally **acknowledged** that _____

DISCUSS & WRITE EXAMPLES
Discuss your response with a partner. Then complete the sentence in writing.

School administrators were forced to **acknowledge** that _____

was a serious problem when some students _____

_____

Write your response and read it aloud to a partner.

Many teens are _____ that they need to _____

_____ if they want to go to college.

Section Shrink

BUILD FLUENCY
Read Section 2 of "Is 16 Too Young to Drive a Car?" (*Issues*, pp. 42–45).

IDENTIFY KEY IDEAS & DETAILS
Take turns asking and answering questions with a partner. Then write brief notes.

Discussion Frames	Text Notes
Q: What is this section **mainly about**? A: This section is **mainly about** _____.	• laws and brain _____ related to _____
Q: What are the **key details** in this section? A: (One/Another) **key detail** in this section is _____. A: Perhaps the **most important key detail** in this section is _____.	• lawmakers concerned with _____ _____ • fatal crashes often caused by _____ _____ not lack of _____ • critical part of _____ underdeveloped until _____

SUMMARIZE
"Shrink" Section 2 of the text by writing a summary in 40 or fewer words.

CLASS SUMMARY: **WORD COUNT:** _____

Lawmakers, who are more concerned with _____ parents

than with reducing _____ won't change driving-age laws

even though researchers acknowledge that _____

occur because the _____

that thinks about consequences doesn't mature until age 25.

PARTNER SUMMARY: **WORD COUNT:** _____

Lawmakers, who are more worried about troubling parents than the safety of _____

_____ refuse to raise the _____ despite

research proving that young drivers have a lack of _____

_____ in the part of the brain that _____

_____

IDENTIFY PRECISE WORDS
Review Section 2 and your *Portfolio* (pp. 94–95) to identify words for your writing.

Topic Words	High-Utility Academic Words
• legislators	• encounter
•	•
•	•

Words to Go

 BUILD WORD KNOWLEDGE

Complete the meanings and examples for these high-utility academic words.

Words to Go	Meanings	Examples
enforce en·force *verb*	to make sure that a law or rule is _____	School security guards **enforce** the rules about _____ _____
enforcement en·force·ment *noun*	the act of making people obey a _____ _____	The strict **enforcement** of the school dress code means I _____

💬 **DISCUSS & WRITE EXAMPLES**

Discuss your response with a partner. Then complete the sentence in writing.

Many schools are **enforcing** rules against _____

by conducting random _____

Write your response and read it aloud to a partner.

The _____ of laws against _____

has helped to _____

 BUILD WORD KNOWLEDGE

Complete the meanings and examples for these high-utility academic words.

Words to Go	Meanings	Examples
advocate ad·vo·cate *noun*	a person who publicly _____ an idea or plan	Now that I know about _____ _____ I plan to become an **advocate** for _____ _____
advocate ad·vo·cate *verb*	to support or _____ an idea or plan	Why do you **advocate** _____ _____ _____

💬 **DISCUSS & WRITE EXAMPLES**

Discuss your response with a partner. Then complete the sentence in writing.

Later this week, the school administration will hear from several **advocates** for

_____

Write your response and read it aloud to a partner.

A group of students is _____ for _____

_____ for all of the school sports teams.

Section Shrink

 BUILD FLUENCY

Read Section 3 of "Is 16 Too Young to Drive a Car?" (*Issues*, pp. 45–47).

 IDENTIFY KEY IDEAS & DETAILS

Take turns asking and answering questions with a partner. Then write brief notes.

Discussion Frames	Text Notes
Q: What is this section **mainly about**? A: This section is **mainly about** _____.	• efforts to understand the _____ and make _____

Q: What are the **key details** in this section?
 	
A: (One/Another) **key detail** in this section is _____.
 	
A: Perhaps the **most important key detail** in this section is _____.
	• hormones can cause teens to make
	
	  _____ decisions
	
	• "graduated licensing" rules restrict _____
	
	  _____ but parents may not
	
	  _____
	
	• safety _____ say more brain
	
	  research and public support necessary to get
	
	  _____ to change laws

 SUMMARIZE

"Shrink" Section 3 of the text by writing a summary in 40 or fewer words.

CLASS SUMMARY: **WORD COUNT:** _____

Teen drivers have difficulty making _____ due to

_____ and brain development, which has led to legal

restrictions on how and when teens _____

and safety advocates calling for _____

PARTNER SUMMARY   **WORD COUNT:** _____

The struggle that teen drivers have controlling their _____

is fueled by hormones and _____

and has resulted in some _____ being placed on

them; but safety experts want additional _____

conducted and support for _____

IDENTIFY PRECISE WORDS

Review Section 3 and your *Portfolio* (pp. 96–97) to identify words for your writing.

Topic Words	High-Utility Academic Words
• thrill-seeking	• in theory
•	•
•	•

Student Writing Model

Academic Writing Type

A **formal written summary** provides an objective overview of the topic and important details from an informational text. The writer credits the author, but writes in primarily his or her own words, without including personal opinions.

  A. The **topic sentence** includes the text type, title, author, and topic.
  B. **Detail sentences** include the important details from the summarized text.
  C. The **concluding sentence** restates the author's conclusion in the writer's own words.

ANALYZE TEXT

Read this student model to analyze the elements of a formal summary.

A   In the magazine article titled "DN'T TXT N DRV," Nancy Mann Jackson explores facts about texting while driving and its potentially fatal consequences.

B   To begin with, Jackson points out that 1.6 million vehicle crashes every year are due to texting or speaking on a cell phone, with high percentages of 16- and 17-year-old drivers admitting to both practices. The author also explains that texting is the most hazardous distraction drivers face because it requires them to take their focus off the road for longer than other distractions, such as eating or changing the radio station. In addition, she reports that lawmakers have responded to the increase in fatal accidents caused by teens by banning the use of cell phones and smart phones while driving. Furthermore, the author describes how some teens are avoiding distractions by shutting off their phones or informing people of their unavailability before getting behind the wheel.

C   Finally, Jackson concludes that teens can advocate for safety by speaking up when friends attempt to text and drive.

MARK & DISCUSS ELEMENTS

Mark the summary elements and use the frames to discuss them with your partner.

1. **Number (1–4) the four elements of the topic sentence.**
   The topic sentence includes the _____.

2. **Draw a box around four transition words or phrases.**
   One transition (word/phrase) is _____.

3. **Underline four important details.** *One important detail in this summary is _____.*

4. **Circle four citation verbs.** *One citation verb that the writer uses is _____.*

5. **Star four precise topic words and check four high-utility academic words.**
   An example of a (precise topic word/high-utility academic word) is _____.

Organize a Formal Summary

Prompt	Write a formal summary of "Is 16 Too Young to Drive a Car?"

Guidelines for Paraphrasing Multiple Sentences

Paraphrase related details from a source text by combining key information into one sentence. Replace key words and phrases with synonyms and keep important topic words.

Text Detail 1	Text Detail 2	Text Detail 3
"A crucial part of the teen's brain—the area that peers ahead and considers consequences—remains undeveloped" (Davis 29).	"…careless attitudes and rash emotions often drive teen decisions, says Jay Giedd, chief of brain imaging in the child psychiatric unit …" (Davis 29).	"…that part of the brain involved in decision-making and controlling impulses is among the latest to come on board" (Davis 30).

PARAPHRASE IDEAS

Combine key information from the three text details above into one detail sentence.

Teen driver errors are linked to underdevelopment in the part of the brain that

(Text Detail 1) _____

(Text Detail 2) _____ and

(Text Detail 3) _____

PLAN KEY IDEAS & DETAILS

State the text information to write a topic sentence.

In the news article titled (title) _____

(author's full name) _____ (citation verb: investigates, explains)

_____ (topic) _____

_____

List four important details from the article using primarily your own words.

1. _____

_____

2. _____

_____

3. _____

_____

4. _____

_____

Restate the author's conclusion in your own words.

_____

_____

Write a Formal Summary

Prompt | Write a formal summary of "Is 16 Too Young to Drive a Car?"

✎ **WRITE A PARAGRAPH**
Use the frame to write your topic sentence, detail sentences, and concluding sentence.

A

In the news article titled _____
(title)

_____ _____
(author's full name) _(citation verb)_

(topic) _____

_____

B

_____ _____ _____
(Transition) _(author's last name)_ _(citation verb)_

(1st important detail) _____

_____

_____

The (author/writer) _____ also _____
(citation verb)

(2nd important detail) _____

_____

_____

_____ (he/she) _____
(Transition) _(citation verb)_

(3rd important detail) _____

_____

_____

_____ the (author/writer) _____
(Transition)

(citation verb) _(4th important detail)_ _____

_____

_____

_____

C

_____ _____ concludes that
(Transition) _(author's last name)_

(restate author's conclusion) _____

_____

_____

Rate Your Summary

Scoring Guide	
1	Insufficient
2	Developing
3	Sufficient
4	Exemplary

ASSESS YOUR DRAFT

Rate your formal summary. Then have a partner rate it.

1. Does the topic sentence state the title, author, and topic?	Self	1	2	3	4
	Partner	1	2	3	4
2. Did you paraphrase the most important details from the text?	Self	1	2	3	4
	Partner	1	2	3	4
3. Did you use citation verbs to credit the author?	Self	1	2	3	4
	Partner	1	2	3	4
4. Did you use transitions to introduce and sequence details?	Self	1	2	3	4
	Partner	1	2	3	4
5. Did you include precise topic words and high-utility academic words?	Self	1	2	3	4
	Partner	1	2	3	4
6. Did you restate the author's conclusion using your own words?	Self	1	2	3	4
	Partner	1	2	3	4

REFLECT & REVISE

Record specific priorities and suggestions to help you and your partner revise.

(Partner) Positive Feedback: I appreciate how you (used/included) _____

_____

_____

(Partner) Suggestion: As you revise your summary, focus on _____

_____

_____

(Self) Priority 1: My summary paragraph needs _____

_____

_____

(Self) Priority 2: I plan to improve my summary by _____

_____

_____

CHECK & EDIT

Use this checklist to proofread and edit your summary.

- ☐ Did you capitalize the title of the article and proper nouns?
- ☐ Did you put quotation marks around the title of the article?
- ☐ Did you use commas appropriately after transitions?
- ☐ Do simple present-tense verbs end in –s?
- ☐ Is each sentence complete?
- ☐ Are all words spelled correctly?

Academic Discussion

What are the reasons why adolescent drivers are at a higher risk for car accidents?

 BRAINSTORM IDEAS

Briefly record at least two ideas in each column using everyday English.

Biological Reasons	Environmental Reasons
• brain development	• not enough practice
•	•
•	•

 ANALYZE WORDS

Complete the chart with precise words to discuss and write about the topic.

Everyday	Precise
very *(adverb)*	exceptionally,
fast *(adjective)*	abruptly,
well *(adverb)*	adequately,

✎ **MAKE A CLAIM**

Rewrite two ideas using the frames and precise words. Then prepare to elaborate verbally.

Language to ELABORATE

In particular, _____.

I have noticed that _____.

1. **Frame:** One (biological/environmental) reason why adolescent drivers are at higher risk for car accidents is that they _____ (**verb phrase:** don't have experience, are immature, lack driving skills)

   Response: _____

   _____

2. **Frame:** Due to _____ (**noun phrase:** brain development, distracted driving, impulsive behavior) adolescent drivers are at higher risk for car accidents.

   Response: _____

   _____

 COLLABORATE

Listen attentively, restate, and record your partner's ideas.

Language to RESTATE

So your perspective is that _____.

Yes, that's correct.

No, not quite. What I (reported/expressed) was _____.

Classmate's Name	Ideas
	1.
	2.

Ten-Minute Paper

A **ten-minute paper** begins with a well-stated **claim** followed by **two detail sentences** that elaborate with relevant examples and precise words.

 PRESENT IDEAS

Listen attentively and take notes. Then indicate if you agree (+) or disagree (–).

Classmate's Name	Idea	+/–

ELABORATE IN WRITING

Work with the teacher to write a ten-minute paper.

One biological reason why adolescent drivers are at higher risk for car accidents is that they have hormone levels that make it difficult to control their emotions. For example, when another driver cut off my 16-year-old cousin, he thought he could get revenge by _____

_____

As a result, when the other driver _____
my cousin _____

_____

Work with a partner to write a ten-minute paper.

Due to _____ adolescent drivers are

at a remarkably higher risk for car accidents. For example, _____

_____

As a result, _____

_____

Words to Go

 BUILD WORD KNOWLEDGE

Complete the meaning and examples for this high-utility academic word.

Word to Go	Meaning	Examples
incidence in·ci·dence *noun*	the _____ _____ something unpleasant happens	Being able to access the internet on cell phones has increased the **incidence of** _____ at school. There's been an unusually high **incidence** of _____ in our community lately.

DISCUSS & WRITE EXAMPLES

Discuss your response with a partner. Then complete the sentence in writing.

The growing **incidence** of _____ in this country is most likely

linked to _____

Write your response and read it aloud to a partner.

What steps can schools take to decrease the _____ of teens

_____

BUILD WORD KNOWLEDGE

Complete the meanings and examples for these high-utility academic words.

Words to Go	Meanings	Examples
violate vi·o·late *verb*	to _____ or _____ a promise, rule, or law	If you _____ _____ you will **violate** my privacy.
violation vi·o·la·tion *noun*	an action that breaks or ignores _____ _____	When I _____ _____ it was a **violation** of my parents' trust.

DISCUSS & WRITE EXAMPLES

Discuss your response with a partner. Then complete the sentence in writing.

It is my opinion that _____

in schools **violates** students' _____

Write your response and read it aloud to a partner.

Some people think _____

is not a serious offense, but I believe it is a terrible _____ of a

person's _____

Close Reading

 BUILD FLUENCY

Read the text "Unsafe Behind the Wheel?" (*Issues*, pp. 48–51).

IDENTIFY KEY IDEAS & DETAILS

Take turns asking and answering questions with a partner. Then write brief notes.

Discussion Frames	Text Notes
Q: What is the author's **main idea**? A: The author's **main idea** is _____.	• restrictions against _____ _____
Q: What are the **key details** in this text? A: One **key details** in this text is _____. A: Another **key details** in this text is _____.	• teen driving restrictions reduce _____ • Congress trying to strengthen teen driving _____ and anti-texting laws • opponents say tagging teen cars violates _____; many think _____ more important

 RESPOND WITH EVIDENCE

Use the frames and evidence from the text to construct a formal written response.

1. Based on the text, what do some of the restrictions against adolescent drivers involve?

   Based on the text, one of the restrictions against adolescent drivers involves

   _____

   Another restriction involves _____

   _____

Use the frames to analyze the structure of the text.

2. In the first two paragraphs, the author contrasts the way teenagers once celebrated being able to drive with the dangers and limitations they face today. Why does the author establish this contrast at the beginning of the text?

   By establishing this contrast at the beginning of the text, the author lets readers know that _____

   _____

IDENTIFY PRECISE WORDS

Review Text 3 and your *Portfolio* (pp. 102–105) to identify words for your writing.

Topic Words	High-Utility Academic Words
• probationary period	• forbid
•	•
•	•

Take a Stand

Debate | Should your state increase the minimum driving age?

 COLLABORATE
Read the debate question about increasing the driving age. Then take turns using a frame to respond with your initial reaction.

ANALYZE SOURCES
Read a quote that either supports or opposes the debate topic. Then paraphrase.

Quote	Paraphrase
Model: "Driving is a new skill for teens, so doing multiple things simultaneously takes more effort for them than for more experienced drivers" (Jackson 36).	In this quote, the author states that teen drivers are _____ so _____ is more challenging for them.
1. "'We have parents who are pretty much tired of chauffeuring their kids around, and they want their children to be able to drive'" (Davis 41).	In other words, some parents are _____ by driving their teens places and would prefer that they acquire _____
2. "Sixteen-year-old drivers are involved in fatal crashes at a rate nearly five times the rate of drivers 20 or older" (Davis 41).	In this quote, the author states that adult drivers cause far fewer _____ than _____
3. "A 2011 study in The Journal of the American Medical Association suggests that restrictions for young drivers may lead to a higher incidence of fatal accidents for 18-year-olds, possibly because they didn't get enough practical driving experience earlier" (Zernike 49).	In other words, a study found that _____ teens from getting a license until age 18 may increase the number of _____ for 18-year-olds since they haven't had _____
4. "'The reality is, when teen drivers crash, it's people in other cars or teen passengers who end up dying,' says Justin McNaull of the auto club AAA, which supports passenger limits to age 21 or even 25" (Zernike 50).	In other words, AAA is an advocate for _____ in cars driven by young people because the _____ are often their teen passengers or other motorists on the road.

Debate Ideas

 SYNTHESIZE IDEAS

Write a response to the debate question, including a paraphrase of a text quote and elaboration on the quote.

Claim: My position is that our state (should/should not) _____ increase the minimum driving age.

Transitional Statement: I have (one key reason/a compelling reason) _____ for taking this stance.

Quote Paraphrase: (According to _____,/The author points out _____.)

_____

_____

_____

Quote Elaboration: (As a result, _____./Consequently, _____.)

_____

_____

_____

 PRESENT EVIDENCE

Ensuring Clear Pronunciation

When presenting ideas during class or in a meeting, ensure **clear pronunciation.** When you speak, make sure that you don't mumble and that you pronounce sounds and words properly so that your audience understands you. For example, make sure you say "going to" instead of "gonna."

LISTEN & TAKE NOTES

Listen attentively and take notes.
Then indicate if you agree (+) or disagree (–).

Language to AFFIRM & CLARIFY

I see what you mean.
One question I have is _____.

Classmate's Name	Idea	+/–

Student Writing Model

Academic Writing Type

A **justification essay** states a claim and supports it with logical reasons and relevant evidence from texts.

> **A.** The **thesis statement** clearly states the writer's claim and tells what the writer will explain about the topic.
>
> **B. Supporting paragraphs** support the claim with reasons and evidence from texts.
>
> **C.** The **conclusion statement** restates the writer's claim about the issue.

🔍 ANALYZE TEXT

Read this student model to analyze the elements of a justification essay.

A

After analyzing research on teens and driving, I disagree entirely that states should increase the minimum driving age.

B

One reason I maintain this position is because increasing the driving age might also increase the number of 18-year-old drivers in fatal accidents. In "Unsafe Behind the Wheel," Kate Zernike presents compelling data regarding the serious consequences of raising the driving age to 18. The author points out a 2011 study that argues that raising the driving age to 18 will only increase the number of fatal accidents involving 18-year-old drivers because they will be inexperienced (Zernike 49). This is significant because one of the main reasons for increasing the driving age is to reduce the number of fatalities, but in reality, it might just change which age group has the most traffic-related deaths.

Another fundamental reason I hold this position is that taking away 16-year-olds' right to drive would inconvenience parents. According to Robert Davis, many legislators and parents have resisted increasing the minimum driving age because they are "tired of chauffeuring their kids around" (41). This evidence underscores the need for 16-year-olds to be able to drive themselves unsupervised.

In addition, my own relevant experience as a teen with an after-school job has made me critically aware that 16- and 17-year-olds should be permitted to drive. As an illustration, my after-school job is located far from my home and school. There is no public transportation and my parents are unavailable to drive me to work. This is proof that 16- and 17-year-olds need to be allowed to drive so that they are able to get to their jobs and earn money.

C

For these reasons, I contend that the minimum driving age should not be raised above 16.

MARK & DISCUSS ELEMENTS
Mark the justification elements and use the frames to discuss them with your partner.

1. **Circle the writer's claim within the thesis statement.**
   The writer's claim is _____.

2. **Draw a box around five transition words or phrases.**
   One transition (word/phrase) is _____.

3. **Underline and label three reasons that support the writer's claim with the letter R.**
   One reason that supports the writer's claim is _____.

4. **Underline and label three pieces of evidence that support the writer's claim with the letter E.** *One piece of evidence that supports the writer's claim is _____.*

5. **Star four precise topic words and check four high-utility academic words.**
   An example of a (precise topic word/high-utility academic word) is _____.

ASSESS A STUDENT SAMPLE
Read an additional student model and rate it.

	Scoring Guide		
1	Insufficient	3	Sufficient
2	Developing	4	Exemplary

1. Does the thesis statement clearly state the claim?	1	2	3	4
2. Do supporting paragraphs begin with a topic sentence that specifies a reason?	1	2	3	4
3. Did the writer give evidence drawn primarily from sources to support the claim?	1	2	3	4
4. Did the writer explain why the evidence is relevant and significant?	1	2	3	4
5. Did the writer use strong verbs to state and restate the claim?	1	2	3	4
6. Did the writer use transitions to introduce reasons and evidence?	1	2	3	4
7. Did the writer include precise topic words and high-utility words?	1	2	3	4
8. Does the conclusion statement strongly restate the claim using new wording?	1	2	3	4

REFLECT & REVISE
Record specific priorities and suggestions to help the writer.

The writer did an effective job of (organizing/including/stating) _____

_____

_____

One way the writer could make the justification essay stronger is _____

_____

_____

I noticed that the writer (forgot to/included/used) _____

_____

_____

This will support me with writing a justification essay because I will remember to _____

_____

_____

Language for Quantity & Frequency

Reason (Why?)	Quantity (How many?)	Frequency (How often?)	Examples
because	few	never	**Many** teens are pledging to drive phone-free **because** they **never** want to be distracted while driving.
since	some	rarely	
due to	several	occasionally	**Since** teens **regularly** get up early for school, **most** are sleep deprived.
as a result of	many	frequently	
	nearly all	regularly	**As a result of** teens **frequently** having accidents at night, **nearly all** states have restrictions on nighttime driving.
	most	usually	
	every	always	

 USE PRECISE LANGUAGE

Rewrite each simple sentence as a complex sentence, using the reason, quantity, and frequency words in parentheses.

Simple Sentence: Students have trouble getting to bed early.

Complex Sentence: **Many** students **regularly** have trouble getting to bed early **since** they do not feel sleepy until later in the night.

1. Teens don't get enough sleep. (*as a result of, few, regularly*)

_____

_____

2. Getting enough sleep is challenging for teens. (*because, most, frequently*)

_____

_____

3. Teens who are sleep deprived exhibit signs of depression. (*due to, some, regularly*)

_____

_____

Add reason, quantity, and frequency to each simple sentence using the chart above.

4. Texting while driving is dangerous.

_____

_____

5. Teen drivers are impulsive.

_____

_____

6. States have enacted Graduated Driver Licensing laws.

_____

_____

Citing Sources

Guidelines for Citing Sources

Citations give credit for other people's ideas. They also help readers find the original information if they want to learn more.

To **cite a source,** use quotation marks around direct quotes or paraphrase the author's ideas in your own words. Identify the source in parentheses and put the period after the citation.

Type of Citation	Guidelines	Examples
when a source has one author	include the author's last name followed by the page number	A study by the National Sleep Foundation found that 15 percent of students reported falling asleep in school over the past year (Weir 5). This is worrisome because sleep-deprived students may have "problems with learning and memory" (Weir 7).
when the author's name is in the sentence	include the page number(s) only	According to Denise Grady, adolescents' demanding schedules often conflict with their internal clocks (8–9).
when a source has two authors	include the authors' last names in the same order as the source	Many schools have cut foreign language classes due to tighter budgets (Altschuler and Skorton 21).

WRITE CITATIONS

Rewrite each sentence with a citation and proper punctuation.

1. Approximately 26 percent of 16- and 17-year-olds have "texted from behind the wheel."

   Text 1: "DN'T TXT N DRV" by Nancy Mann Jackson

   _____

   _____

2. Scientists have discovered that the part of the brain that is "involved in decision-making and controlling impulses" is the last to develop.

   Text 2: "Is 16 Too Young to Drive a Car?" by Robert Davis

   _____

   _____

3. According to Kate Zernike, teens have more trouble with multitasking when they are behind the wheel.

   Text 3: "Unsafe Behind the Wheel?" by Kate Zernike

   _____

   _____

Organize a Justification Essay

Prompt	Should your state increase the minimum driving age? Write a justification essay that states and supports your claim.

Thesis Starters	Examples
After analyzing the research on . . . After reviewing the (evidence, data) on . . . After examining the issues surrounding . . .	**After analyzing the research on** teen sleep, I agree wholeheartedly that schools should start later to accommodate teen sleep needs. **After reviewing the data on** adolescent sleep needs, I believe strongly that schools should not start later.
Conclusion Starters	**Examples**
For these reasons, In light of this evidence,	**For these reasons,** I conclude that foreign language class should not be a mandatory component of a high school's curriculum. **In light of this evidence,** I maintain that foreign language should be a required class in high school.

✎ WRITE A THESIS STATEMENT
Describe your claim.

My claim: _____

_____

Use academic language to restate your claim as a thesis statement.

_____ adolescents and driving,

(Thesis starter)

I (agree/disagree) _____ (strongly, firmly) _____

that _____

(your claim)

💡 CHOOSE SUPPORTING TOPICS
List each topic you will write about to support your claim.
Supporting Paragraph 1

Topic: _____

_____

Supporting Paragraph 2

Topic: _____

_____

Supporting Paragraph 3

Topic: _____

_____

PLAN SUPPORTING PARAGRAPHS

List reasons and evidence that support your claim. You may draw from texts, your experience, or a classmate's experience.

Supporting Paragraph 1

Reason 1: _____

_____

Evidence: _____

_____

Source: _____

Author: _____

Elaboration on this evidence: _____

_____

_____

Supporting Paragraph 2

Reason 2: _____

_____

Evidence: _____

_____

Source: _____

Author: _____

Elaboration on this evidence: _____

_____

_____

Supporting Paragraph 3

Reason 3: _____

_____

Relevant personal experience: _____

_____

Relevant personal connection: _____

Elaboration on this evidence: _____

_____

WRITE A CONCLUSION

Plan a conclusion statement that restates your claim.

_____ I contend that

(Conclusion starter)

_____

Write a Justification Essay

Prompt Should your state increase the minimum driving age? Write a justification essay that states and supports your claim.

 WRITE AN ESSAY

Use the frame to write your thesis statement, supporting paragraphs, and conclusion statement.

A

(Thesis starter)
_____
adolescents and driving, I (agree/disagree) _____
(strongly, firmly) _____ that _____
(claim)
_____
_____
_____

B1

One reason I maintain this position is _____
(1st reason that supports your claim)
_____
_____
_____

In _____
(title of source)
_____ presents (strong, convincing, compelling)
(author's name)
_____ (data, statistics, evidence) _____
regarding the (positive, negative, serious) _____ consequences of
_____
(topic)
_____

The author points out that _____
(text evidence)
_____
_____
_____
_____

This is significant because _____
(elaborate on text evidence)
_____
_____
_____

B2

Another (important, fundamental, critical) _____ reason I hold this position is that _____
(2nd reason that supports your claim)

_____

_____

_____

According to _____
(source or author's name)

_____
(text evidence)

_____

_____

This (data, evidence) _____ underscores (the need for, the impact of, the seriousness of) _____
(elaborate on text evidence)

_____

_____

B3

In addition, my own relevant experience as _____
(relevant personal connection)

_____

has made me critically aware that _____
(claim)

_____

_____

_____

As an illustration, _____
(relevant personal experience)

_____

_____

_____

This is (evidence, proof) _____ that _____
(elaborate on personal experience)

_____

_____

C

_____ I contend that
(Conclusion starter)

_____
(restate your claim)

_____

_____

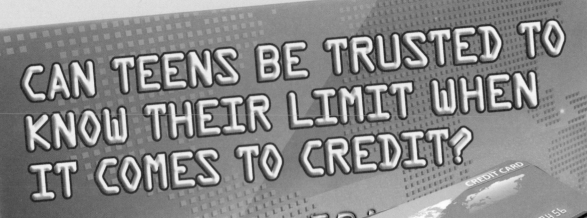

CAN TEENS BE TRUSTED TO KNOW THEIR LIMIT WHEN IT COMES TO CREDIT?

4321 9876 50

BUILD KNOWLEDGE
Read and respond to the Data File (*Issues*, p. 52).

BRAINSTORM IDEAS
Write a brief list of similarities and differences between credit and cash.

- difference: credit must be paid back
- _____
- _____
- _____

PRESENT IDEAS
Use the frames to discuss ideas with your group. Listen attentively and record the strongest ideas to complete the diagram.

> **Language to FACILITATE DISCUSSION**
> So, _____, what's your perspective?
> _____, what (similarity/difference) did you come up with?

1. Cash and credit are similar in that they both _____ (**present-tense verb:** allow)
2. One difference between them is that (cash/credit) _____ (**present-tense verb:** requires)
3. Another way they are different is that (cash/credit) _____ (**present-tense verb:** can be)
4. Teens might use (cash/credit) because it _____ (**present-tense verb:** buys)

CREDIT
- can result in interest charges

BOTH
- are available in limited amounts

CASH
- cannot lead to overspending

Words to Know

BUILD WORD KNOWLEDGE

Rate your word knowledge. Then discuss word meanings and examples with your group.

		① Don't Know	② Recognize	③ Familiar	④ Know

Word to Know	Meaning	Examples
1 **debt** *noun* ① ② ③ ④	_____ or something else that is _____ and should be paid back	My sister did me a huge favor, so I _____ _____ _____ to repay the **debt**.
2 **financial** *adjective* ① ② ③ ④	relating to the management and use of _____	My _____ _____ has brought me some **financial** success.
3 **interest** *noun* ① ② ③ ④	the extra money paid for _____ money	The loan I plan to take out for _____ has a low rate of **interest**.
4 **credit** *noun* ① ② ③ ④	an agreement that allows you to _____ something and pay for it _____	Many people use **credit** to make large purchases, such as _____ _____ _____
1 **balance** *noun* ① ② ③ ④	the remaining amount of money that is still _____	Once I pay off the **balance** on _____ _____ _____ I will be able to start saving again.
2 **income** *noun* ① ② ③ ④	money that a person _____ from a job or other source	_____ _____ is a great way for teens to earn some extra **income** during the summer.
3 **fee** *noun* ① ② ③ ④	the amount of money _____ for a service	_____ often charge an extra **fee** for_____ _____ _____
4 **bankrupt** *adjective* ① ② ③ ④	without enough _____ to pay what is owed	When the company went **bankrupt**, it had to _____ court.

Academic Discussion
WHAT ARE SOME WAYS ADOLESCENTS EARN AND SPEND INCOME?

 BRAINSTORM IDEAS

Briefly record at least two ideas in each column using everyday English.

Income	Expenses
• receiving birthday money • •	• gas or public transportation • •

 ANALYZE WORDS

Complete the chart with precise words to discuss and write about the topic.

Everyday	Precise
cost *(noun)*	expense,
work *(verb)*	to be employed,
buy *(verb)*	procure,

 MAKE A CLAIM

Rewrite two ideas using the frames and precise words. Then prepare to elaborate verbally.

Language to ELABORATE

As an illustration, _____.

I have discovered that _____.

1. **Frame:** In my experience, adolescents (earn/spend) income by _____ (**verb + –ing:** babysitting, doing chores, buying clothes)

   Response: _____

   _____

2. **Frame:** A common (source of income/expense) for adolescents is _____ (**noun:** allowance, a part-time job, bus fare)

   Response: _____

   _____

 COLLABORATE

Listen attentively, restate, and record your partner's idea.

Language to RESTATE

So your point of view is that _____.

Yes, that's correct.

No, not quite. What I (expressed/suggested) is that _____.

Classmate's Name	Ideas
	1.
	2.

Ten-Minute Paper

A **ten-minute paper** begins with a **claim,** followed by **two detail sentences** that elaborate with relevant examples and precise words.

 PRESENT IDEAS

Listen, compare ideas, and take notes. Then indicate if you agree (+) or disagree (–).

Classmate's Name	Idea	+/–

ELABORATE IN WRITING

Work with the teacher to write a ten-minute paper.

In my experience, adolescents spend income by keeping up with the latest fashions. For example, when a certain brand of _____

(is/are) extremely _____ teens may

feel _____ to own them. As a result,

teens may have to pay a high _____

to _____ them.

Work with a partner to write a ten-minute paper.

A common _____ for adolescents is

_____

For example, when teens _____

_____

they may _____

_____

As a result, teens may end up _____

in exchange for _____

Words to Go

BUILD WORD KNOWLEDGE

Complete the meanings and examples for these high-utility words.

Words to Go	Meanings	Examples
minimum min·i·mum *noun/adjective*	the _____ amount allowed or needed; describing the smallest _____ allowed or needed	I need a minimum of _____ _____ to _____ I meet the minimum age for _____ _____ _____
minimize min·i·mize *verb*	to _____ something as much as possible	To minimize costs, I _____ _____ _____

DISCUSS & WRITE EXAMPLES

Discuss your response with a partner. Then complete the sentence in writing.

I _____ to meet the **minimum**

requirement for admission to _____

Write your response and read it aloud to a partner.

Many schools are eliminating _____

_____ in an effort to _____ the negative impact

_____

BUILD WORD KNOWLEDGE

Complete the meaning and example for this high-utility word.

Word to Go	Meaning	Examples
evaluate e·val·u·ate *verb*	to decide how _____ or _____ something is	In class, we evaluate _____ _____ with a rubric.

DISCUSS & WRITE EXAMPLES

Discuss your response with a partner. Then complete the sentence in writing.

The city **evaluated** the mural we painted, and decided that it was _____

_____

Write your response and read it aloud to a partner.

After _____ the student's online behavior, the principal came to

the conclusion that _____

Close Reading

 BUILD FLUENCY

Read the text "Buyer, Beware!" (*Issues*, pp. 53–57).

 IDENTIFY KEY IDEAS & DETAILS

Take turns asking and answering questions with a partner. Then write brief notes.

Discussion Frames	Text Notes
Q: What is the author's **main idea**? A: The author's **main idea** is _____.	• _____ can be helpful but _____
Q: What are the **key details** in this text? A: (One/Another) **key detail** in this text is _____.	• credit good for _____ or getting _____ • _____ or fees on credit not _____ or on time create more _____ • bad _____ could cost you a _____ or _____

RESPOND WITH EVIDENCE

Use the frames and evidence from the text to construct a formal written response.

1. According to the author, what are some dangers to avoid when using a credit card?

   According to the author, dangers to avoid when using a credit card include _____

   _____

   In addition, users should avoid making only minimum payments because _____

   _____

Use the frame to analyze the author's development of ideas.

2. Why does the author include the anecdote about Sanyika Galloway Boyce?

   The author includes the anecdote about Boyce to help the reader understand

   _____

   It allows the reader to imagine _____

   _____

 IDENTIFY PRECISE WORDS

Review Text 1 and your *Portfolio* (pp. 116–121) to identify words for your writing.

Topic Words	High-Utility Academic Words
• interest rate	• unnecessary
•	•
•	•

Academic Discussion
WHAT ARE THE BENEFITS AND DRAWBACKS OF USING A CREDIT CARD?

 BRAINSTORM IDEAS

Briefly record at least two ideas in each column using everyday English.

Benefits	Drawbacks
• earn cash back	• can go over budget
•	•
•	•

 ANALYZE WORDS

Complete the chart with precise words to discuss and write about the issue.

Everyday	Precise
forget *(verb)*	neglect,
go over *(verb)*	exceed,
set up *(verb)*	establish,

 MAKE A CLAIM

Rewrite two ideas using the frames and precise words. Then prepare to elaborate verbally.

1. **Frame:** One (benefit/drawback) of using a credit card is _____ (**verb + –ing**: establishing credit, paying interest, overspending)

   Response: _____

   _____

2. **Frame:** Using a credit card can be (beneficial/harmful) when you _____ (**verb phrase**: incur fees, build credit history, pay only the minimum)

   Response: _____

   _____

Language to ELABORATE
As an illustration, _____.
I have discovered that _____.

 COLLABORATE

Listen attentively, restate, and record your partner's idea.

Classmate's Name	Ideas
	1.
	2.

Language to RESTATE
So your point of view is that _____.
Yes, that's correct.
No, not quite. What I (expressed/suggested) is that _____.

Ten-Minute Paper

A **ten-minute paper** begins with a **claim**, followed by **two detail sentences** that elaborate with relevant examples and precise words.

Language to AGREE/DISAGREE

I (agree/disagree) with _____'s point of view about _____.

PRESENT IDEAS

Listen, compare ideas, and take notes. Then indicate if you agree (+) or disagree (–).

Classmate's Name	Idea	+/–

ELABORATE IN WRITING

Work with the teacher to write a ten-minute paper.

Language to COLLABORATE

What should we write?

We could choose _____. What do you think fits logically?

Another possibility is _____.

One _____ of using a credit card is _____ _____ a strong credit score. For example, paying the card's _____ in full every month and never _____ raises your credit score. As a result, future _____ and _____ are more likely to see you as a desirable job candidate or tenant.

Work with a partner to write a ten-minute paper.

Using a credit card can be _____ when you _____ _____

For example, a credit card user might have to _____ _____

As a result, an initial purchase of _____ could end up costing _____

Words to Go

 BUILD WORD KNOWLEDGE

Complete the meanings and examples for these high-utility academic words.

Words to Go	Meanings	Examples
significant sig·nif·i·cant *adjective*	large or _____ enough to have an effect on something	_____ _____ had a **significant** impact on my dream of becoming _____
significantly sig·nif·i·cant·ly *adverb*	in an _____ or _____ way	I knew I had to **significantly** improve my grades if I wanted _____ _____

DISCUSS & WRITE EXAMPLES

Discuss your response with a partner. Then complete the sentence in writing.

Some social networking websites have made **significant** changes to their

_____ in response to _____

Write your response and read it aloud to a partner.

_____

could _____ reduce the number of vehicle crashes involving teens.

BUILD WORD KNOWLEDGE

Complete the meaning and examples for this high-utility academic word.

Word to Go	Meaning	Examples
accurately ac·cu·rate·ly *adverb*	in a way that is _____ and _____ in every detail	To **accurately** measure _____ _____ you should use _____ The _____ _____ was so bizarre that I had trouble **accurately** describing it to my friends.

DISCUSS & WRITE EXAMPLES

Discuss your response with a partner. Then complete the sentence in writing.

Generally, fashion magazines do not **accurately** portray _____

_____

Write your response and read it aloud to a partner.

The victim tried to _____ describe the _____

_____

Section Shrink

 BUILD FLUENCY

Read the introduction and Section 1 of "If at First You Don't Succeed"
(*Issues*, pp. 58–61).

 IDENTIFY KEY IDEAS & DETAILS

Take turns asking and answering questions with a partner. Then write brief notes.

Discussion Frames	Text Notes
Q: What is this section **mainly about**? **A:** This section is **mainly about** _____.	• young adults should _____ financial mistakes involving _____
Q: What are the **key details** in this section? **A:** (One/Another) **key detail** in this section is _____. **A:** Perhaps the **most important key detail** in this section is _____.	• fully repay purchases made with _____ credit cards, or risk increased charges • beware of _____ and correct it _____ • protect your _____ by _____ and _____

 SUMMARIZE

"Shrink" Section 1 of the text by writing a summary in 40 or fewer words.

CLASS SUMMARY   **WORD COUNT:** _____

Manage your _____ and protect _____

by avoiding _____ seeking help for

_____ and paying

credit card bills _____

PARTNER SUMMARY   **WORD COUNT:** _____

Young adults should _____

by _____ not borrowing more money

to _____ and paying _____

_____ on _____

IDENTIFY PRECISE WORDS

Review Section 1 and your *Portfolio* (pp. 122–125) to identify words for your writing.

Topic Words	High-Utility Academic Words
• major purchases • •	• accomplish • •

Words to Go

 BUILD WORD KNOWLEDGE

Complete the meanings and examples for these high-utility academic words.

Words to Go	Meanings	Examples
potential po·ten·tial *adjective/noun*	possible, but not _____ actual or real; the _____ that something will develop in a certain way	The guidance counselor talked to me about **potential** _____ _____ I worry about dating because of the **potential** for _____ _____
potentially po·ten·tial·ly *adverb*	having the possibility of _____ in a certain way	Sleep deprivation is **potentially** harmful to teens' _____ _____

 DISCUSS & WRITE EXAMPLES

Discuss your response with a partner. Then complete the sentence in writing.

Some video games have the **potential** to help teens _____

_____

Write your response and read it aloud to a partner.

_____

is _____ risky for teen drivers.

BUILD WORD KNOWLEDGE

Complete the meaning and examples for this high-utility academic word.

Word to Go	Meaning	Examples
priority pri·or·i·ty *noun*	something that is more _____ than other things	_____ _____ is a **priority** for me. Doing _____ _____ should be my **priority** when I get home from school.

DISCUSS & WRITE EXAMPLES

Discuss your response with a partner. Then complete the sentence in writing.

The top **priorities** for many teens are _____

and _____

Write your response and read it aloud to a partner.

One of the student council's _____ is _____

_____

Section Shrink

 BUILD FLUENCY

Read Section 2 of "If at First You Don't Succeed" (*Issues*, pp. 61–64).

 IDENTIFY KEY IDEAS & DETAILS

Take turns asking and answering questions with a partner.

Discussion Frames	Text Notes
Q: What is this section **mainly about**? A: This section is **mainly about** _____.	• budgeting and long-term _____ _____
Q: What are the **key details** in this section? A: (One/Another) **key detail** in this section is _____. A: Perhaps the **most important key detail** in this section is _____.	• avoid having too many _____ _____ so you don't hurt your chances of getting a good loan • a _____ helps you avoid _____ • saving money for the _____ and making _____ are two ways to _____

 SUMMARIZE

"Shrink" Section 2 of the text by writing a summary in 40 or fewer words.

CLASS SUMMARY   **WORD COUNT:** _____

Limit the _____

you have so banks won't view you as _____

and prioritize your _____ with a _____ that

allows you to _____

PARTNER SUMMARY   **WORD COUNT:** _____

Protect _____

by having _____ credit cards,

creating _____ and depositing money

into _____

IDENTIFY PRECISE WORDS

Review Section 2 and your *Portfolio* (pp. 126–127) to identify words for your writing.

Topic Words	High-Utility Academic Words
• investment	• inclined
•	•
•	•

Words to Go

 BUILD WORD KNOWLEDGE

Complete the meaning and examples for this high-utility academic word.

Word to Go	Meaning	Examples
periodically pe·ri·od·i·cal·ly *adverb*	at _____ times	When I'm working at my computer, I periodically _____ _____ I periodically _____ my cell phone's _____

 DISCUSS & WRITE EXAMPLES

Discuss your response with a partner. Then complete the sentence in writing.

Many students are unhappy that the school district will **periodically** _____

_____

Write your response and read it aloud to a partner.

Family is very important to me, so I _____ visit _____

_____

 BUILD WORD KNOWLEDGE

Complete the meaning and examples for these high-utility academic words.

Words to Go	Meanings	Examples
indication in·di·ca·tion *noun*	a _____ or piece of _____ that points something out	Because her expression gave me no indication of her feelings, I couldn't tell if _____ _____
indicate in·di·cate *verb*	to _____ or _____ something	The _____ coming from the cafeteria indicate that _____ _____

 DISCUSS & WRITE EXAMPLES

Discuss your response with a partner. Then complete the sentence in writing.

All the **indications** suggest a strong connection between _____

_____ and teenagers' eating habits.

Write your response and read it aloud to a partner.

Yesterday, my inability to concentrate in class _____ that I _____

_____

Section Shrink

 BUILD FLUENCY

Read Section 3 of "If at First You Don't Succeed" (*Issues*, pp. 64–66).

 IDENTIFY KEY IDEAS & DETAILS

Take turns asking and answering questions with a partner. Then write brief notes.

Discussion Frames	Text Notes
Q: What is this section **mainly about**? **A:** This section is **mainly about** _____.	• taking _____ for your _____ independence

Q: What are the **key details** in this section?
 	
A: (One/Another) **key detail** in this section is _____.
 	
A: Perhaps the **most important key detail** in this section is _____.
	• use own bank's _____ to
	  minimize _____; don't
	  _____
	• periodically review _____;
	  contact bank to _____
	• take charge by paying _____
	  on credit card bills, _____ more,
	  cutting _____

 SUMMARIZE

"Shrink" Section 3 of the text by writing a summary in 40 or fewer words.

CLASS SUMMARY   **WORD COUNT:** _____

Gain _____ by avoiding ATM

and _____ fees, reviewing your

accounts for _____

paying down _____ and spending _____

PARTNER SUMMARY   **WORD COUNT:** _____

Be financially responsible by using _____

not bouncing _____ saving _____ and

periodically _____

IDENTIFY PRECISE WORDS

Review Section 3 and your *Portfolio* (pp. 128–129) to identify words for your writing.

Topic Words	High-Utility Words
• financial institution	• precaution
•	•
•	•

Student Writing Model

Academic Writing Type

A **formal written summary** provides an objective overview of the topic and important details from an informational text. The writer credits the author, but writes in primarily his or her own words, without including personal opinions.

    A. The **topic sentence** includes the text type, title, author, and topic.
    B. Detail sentences include the important details from the summarized text.
    C. The **concluding sentence** restates the author's conclusion in the writer's own words.

🔍 ANALYZE TEXT

Read this student model to analyze the elements of a formal summary.

A   In the magazine article titled "Buyer, Beware!," Brooke Stephens discusses the important information teens should know about using credit cards. To begin with, Stephens presents an anecdote about a college student whose reckless credit card use led to significant debt. The author also explains that using credit to make major purchases is smart, but using it to buy small items is not **B** the best use of credit cards. Additionally, she emphasizes the importance of paying balances in full each month and not missing any payments so that users avoid interest and late fees. Moreover, the author describes how credit cards influence scores and how bad credit can potentially impact someone's ability to get a job or an apartment. Lastly, Stephens concludes that having one major, **C** universally accepted credit card with a low interest rate is better than having multiple high-interest department store cards.

💬 MARK & DISCUSS ELEMENTS

Mark the summary elements and use the frames to discuss them with your partner.

1. **Number (1–4) the four elements of the topic sentence.** *The topic sentence includes the _____.*

2. **Draw a box around four transition words or phrases.** *One transition (word/phrase) is _____.*

3. **Underline four important details.** *One important detail in this summary is _____.*

4. **Circle four citation verbs.** *One citation verb that the writer uses is _____.*

5. **Star four precise topic words and check four high-utility academic words.** *An example of a (precise topic word/high-utility academic word) is _____.*

Organize a Formal Summary

Prompt Write a formal summary of "If at First You Don't Succeed."

Guidelines for Paraphrasing Multiple Sentences
Paraphrase related details from a source text by combining key information into one sentence. Replace key words and phrases with synonyms and keep important topic words.

Text Detail 1	Text Detail 2	Text Detail 3
"[Signs of a serious debt problem] may include borrowing money to make payments on loans you already have, deliberately paying bills late, and putting off doctor visits . . ." ("If at First" 59).	". . . try to pay off your highest interest-rate loans (usually your credit cards) as soon as possible, even if you have higher balances on other loans" ("If at First" 59).	"Companies called credit bureaus prepare credit reports for use by lenders, employers, insurance companies, landlords, and others who need to know someone's financial reliability . . ." ("If at First" 60).

 PARAPHRASE IDEAS
Combine key information from the three text details above into one detail sentence.

Consumers should watch out for

(Text Detail 1) _____ and focus on

(Text Detail 2) _____ to protect their

(Text Detail 3) _____

PLAN KEY IDEAS & DETAILS
State the text information to write a topic sentence.

In the newsletter titled (title) _____

the author (citation verb: presents, investigates, discusses) _____

(topic) _____

_____

List four important details from the article primarily using your own words.

1. _____

_____

2. _____

_____

3. _____

_____

4. _____

_____

Restate the author's conclusion in your own words.

_____

_____

Write a Formal Summary

Prompt Write a formal summary of "If at First You Don't Succeed."

✏️ WRITE A PARAGRAPH
Use the frame to write your topic sentence, detail sentences, and concluding sentence.

A

In the newsletter titled _____
_____ (title)
_____

the (author/writer) _____ _____
                                              (citation verb)

_____
(topic)

_____

B

_____ the (author/writer) _____
(Transition)

_____ _____
(citation verb)   (1st important detail)

_____

_____

The (author/writer) _____ also _____
                                              (citation verb)

_____
(2nd important detail)

_____

_____

_____ the (author/writer) _____
(Transition)

_____ _____
(citation verb)   (3rd important detail)

_____

_____

_____ the (author/writer) _____
(Transition)

_____ _____
(citation verb)   (4th important detail)

_____

_____

C

_____ the (author/writer) _____
(Transition)

concludes that _____
               (restate author's conclusion)

_____

Rate Your Summary

Scoring Guide	
1	Insufficient
2	Developing
3	Sufficient
4	Exemplary

ASSESS YOUR DRAFT

Rate your formal summary. Then have a partner rate it.

1. Does the topic sentence state the title, author, and topic?	Self	1	2	3	4
	Partner	1	2	3	4
2. Did you paraphrase the most important details from the text?	Self	1	2	3	4
	Partner	1	2	3	4
3. Did you use citation verbs to credit the author?	Self	1	2	3	4
	Partner	1	2	3	4
4. Did you use transitions to introduce and sequence details?	Self	1	2	3	4
	Partner	1	2	3	4
5. Did you include precise topic words and high-utility academic words?	Self	1	2	3	4
	Partner	1	2	3	4
6. Did you restate the author's conclusion using your own words?	Self	1	2	3	4
	Partner	1	2	3	4

REFLECT & REVISE

Record specific priorities and suggestions to help you and your partner revise.

(Partner) Positive Feedback: I appreciate how you (used/included) _____

_____

_____

(Partner) Suggestion: As you revise your summary, focus on _____

_____

_____

(Self) Priority 1: My summary paragraph needs _____

_____

(Self) Priority 2: I plan to improve my summary by _____

_____

CHECK & EDIT

Use this checklist to proofread and edit your formal summary.

☐ Did you capitalize the title of the article and proper nouns?

☐ Did you put quotation marks around the title of the article?

☐ Did you use commas appropriately after transitions?

☐ Do simple present-tense verbs end in –s?

☐ Is each sentence complete?

☐ Are all words spelled correctly?

Academic Discussion

WHAT ARE SOME EXAMPLES OF RESPONSIBLE AND IRRESPONSIBLE FINANCIAL BEHAVIOR?

 BRAINSTORM IDEAS

Briefly record at least two ideas in each column using everyday English.

Responsible Behavior	Irresponsible Behavior
• not overspending	• missing credit card payments
•	•
•	•

 ANALYZE WORDS

Complete the chart with precise words to discuss and write about the topic.

Everyday	Precise
keep to *(verb)*	adhere to,
check *(verb)*	monitor,
habit *(noun)*	routine,

MAKE A CLAIM

Rewrite two ideas using the frames and precise words. Then prepare to elaborate verbally.

Language to ELABORATE

As an illustration, _____.

I have discovered that _____.

1. **Frame:** An example of (responsible/irresponsible) financial behavior is _____ (**verb + –ing**: minimizing expenses, saving for the future, building debt)

   Response: _____

   _____

2. **Frame:** Young adults show (responsible/irresponsible) financial behavior when they _____ (**verb phrase**: avoid fees, save income, pay bills late)

   Response: _____

   _____

 COLLABORATE

Listen attentively, restate, and record your partner's ideas.

Language to RESTATE

So your point of view is that _____.

Yes, that's correct.

No, not quite. What I (expressed/suggested) is that _____.

Classmate's Name	Ideas
	1.
	2.

Ten-Minute Paper

A **ten-minute** paper begins with a **claim,** followed by **two detail sentences** that elaborate with relevant examples and precise words.

 PRESENT IDEAS

Listen, compare ideas, and take notes. Then indicate if you agree (+) or disagree (–).

Classmate's Name	Idea	+/–

ELABORATE IN WRITING
Work with the teacher to write a ten-minute paper.

An example of _____ financial behavior is forgetting to pay credit card bills on time. For example, the _____ forgave my friend for his first late payment, but then he _____ _____

As a result, the bank raised the interest rate on his account and now he _____ _____

Work with a partner to write a ten-minute paper.

Young adults show _____ financial behavior when they make it a practice to _____ _____

For example, _____ _____ _____

As a result, _____ _____

Words to Go

 BUILD WORD KNOWLEDGE

Complete the meaning and examples for this high-utility academic word.

Word to Go	Meaning	Examples
restructure re·struc·ture *verb*	to _____ the way something is organized; to _____ the terms of debts	By borrowing money from _____ _____ I was able to **restructure** my debt. The new _____ plans to **restructure** the school's _____ so that it's more efficient.

 DISCUSS & WRITE EXAMPLES

Discuss your response with a partner. Then complete the sentence in writing.

The club decided to **restructure** its leadership so that _____

_____

Write your response and read it aloud to a partner.

I may not be able to eliminate the money I owe on my credit card, but I can

_____ the debt so that I can _____

 BUILD WORD KNOWLEDGE

Complete the meanings and examples for these high-utility academic words.

Words to Go	Meanings	Examples
promote pro·mote *verb*	to help something become more _____ _____ or well-known	I _____ _____ to **promote** myself when I ran for class president.
promotion pro·mo·tion *noun*	an activity to help something become more successful or _____	As part of the **promotion** for a new movie, the company that made it is giving away _____

 DISCUSS & WRITE EXAMPLES

Discuss your response with a partner. Then complete the sentence in writing.

Magazine advertisements **promoting** _____ often use enhanced

photos so that people will _____

Write your response and read it aloud to a partner.

The local grocery store is giving away tote bags as part of a _____

for _____

Close Reading

BUILD FLUENCY

Read the text "Bankrupt by 25" (*Issues*, pp. 67–69).

IDENTIFY KEY IDEAS & DETAILS

Take turns asking and answering questions with a partner. Then write brief notes.

Discussion Frames	Text Notes
Q: What is the author's **main idea**? A: The author's **main idea** is _____.	• many young adults are declaring _____
Q: What are the **key details** in this text? A: (One/Another) **key detail** in this text is _____.	• some experts say rise due to _____ _____ • others blame increasing _____ _____ and using student-loan money for _____ • some colleges and organizations teach young adults _____

RESPOND WITH EVIDENCE

Use the frames and evidence from the text to construct a formal written response.

1. According to the author, how can the college experience contribute to the potential for young adults to go bankrupt?

    According to the author, _____

    _____ can contribute to the potential for them to go bankrupt.

    In addition, the high cost of tuition forces many students to _____

    _____

Use the frames to analyze the author's word choice.

2. How does the author use the word *stain* in paragraph 5? What is its effect?

    The author uses the word *stain* (literally/figuratively) _____

    because _____

    Using *stain* in this context suggests that bankruptcy _____

    _____

IDENTIFY PRECISE WORDS

Review Text 3 and your *Portfolio* (pp. 134–137) to identify words for your writing.

Topic Words	High-Utility Academic Words
• financial literacy	• aggressive
•	•
•	•

Take a Stand

| Debate | Are adolescents prepared to take on the responsibilities of using credit cards? |

COLLABORATE

Read the debate question about teens and money. Then take turns using a frame to respond with your initial reaction.

Language to RESPOND

So, _____, what's your initial reaction?

My initial reaction is _____.

My initial reaction is (the same/somewhat different).

ANALYZE SOURCES

Read a quote that either supports or opposes the debate question. Then paraphrase.

Quote	Paraphrase
Model: "According to a survey, 77% of teens think they are knowledgeable about how to manage money, including budgets, savings, and investments" (Charles Schwab & Co. 52).	This quote reinforces the idea that more than _____ of adolescents are confident they can _____ their _____
1. "Buying a home, purchasing a car, starting a business, and getting a student loan for college are smart uses of credit" (Stephens 54).	In this quote, the author states that people should use credit for major _____ such as going to college or purchasing _____
2. "'Many young people don't take the time to check their receipts or make the necessary phone calls or write letters to correct a problem'" ("If at First" 65).	This quote reinforces the idea that adolescents often fail to _____ their receipts or contact _____ to correct _____
3. "In 2001, 150,000 people under 25 filed for bankruptcy, a 150 percent increase over 1991" (Smillie 67).	In this quote, the author states that 150,000 _____ had to _____ and the number is _____
4. "The Senate Banking Committee reports that 73 percent of college freshmen used student-loan money to pay off debt, notably credit-card balances" (Smillie 68).	This quote reinforces the idea that most teens in their first year of _____ are using student-loan money for _____ instead of _____

Debate Ideas

 SYNTHESIZE IDEAS

Write a response to the debate question, including a paraphrase of a text quote and elaboration on the quote.

Claim: My position is that adolescents (are/are not) _____ prepared to take on the responsibilities of using a credit card.

Transitional Statement: I have (one key reason/a compelling reason) _____

_____ for taking this stance.

Quote Paraphrase: (According to _____,/The author points out _____.)

_____

_____

_____

Quote Elaboration: (As a result, _____/Consequently, _____.)

_____

_____

_____

 PRESENT EVIDENCE

Speaking at an Appropriate Pace

When presenting ideas during class or in a meeting, speak at an **appropriate pace**. Speak slowly, stop to breathe, and pause briefly to emphasize a point or to avoid inserting fillers such as *um, so,* or *like*.

LISTEN & TAKE NOTES

Listen attentively and take notes. Then indicate if you agree (+) or disagree (–).

> **Language to AFFIRM & CLARIFY**
>
> That's an intriguing perspective.
> I don't quite understand _____.

Classmate's Name	Idea	+/-

Student Writing Model

Academic Writing Type

A **justification essay** states a claim and supports it with logical reasons and relevant evidence from texts.

A. The **thesis statement** clearly states the writer's claim and tells what the writer will explain about the topic.

B. **Supporting paragraphs** support the claim with reasons and evidence from texts.

C. The **conclusion statement** restates the writer's claim about the issue.

ANALYZE TEXT

Read this student model to analyze elements of a justification essay.

A

After analyzing research on teens and money, I agree strongly that adolescents are prepared to take on the responsibilities of using credit cards.

B

One reason I maintain this position is because the majority of teens are not at risk for going into credit card debt. In a 2011 survey of teenagers, Charles Schwab & Co. presents convincing statistics about teens' incomes. The survey points out that more than two-thirds of teens are employed and earn more than $1,000 each year on average (52). This is significant because while some people may argue that teens don't have the resources to stay out of debt if they use a credit card, the reality is that many teens are earning their own money to pay their bills.

Another important reason I hold this position is that even if teens start out with minimal financial know-how, many tools are available to help them. According to Dirk Smillie, numerous organizations offer free financial advice and education (69). This evidence underscores the seriousness of using credit cards while showing that teens have the potential to become responsible credit card users.

In addition, my own relevant experience as the relative of someone who is in debt has made me critically aware that financial responsibility has little to do with age. As an illustration, my uncle went bankrupt because he overspent with credit cards. Conversely, my 19-year-old sister uses a credit card, but her first priority is adding to her savings account each month. This is proof that teens can be trusted with credit cards.

C

For these reasons, I contend that teens can handle the responsibilities that come with using credit cards.

MARK & DISCUSS ELEMENTS

Mark the justification elements and use the frames to discuss them with your partner.

1. **Circle the writer's claim within the thesis statement.** *The writer's claim is _____.*

2. **Draw a box around five transition words or phrases.**
   One transition (word/phrase) is _____.

3. **Underline and label three reasons that support the writer's claim with the letter *R*.**
   One reason that supports the writer's claim is _____.

4. **Underline and label three pieces of evidence that support the writer's claim with the letter *E*.** *One piece of evidence that supports the writer's claim is _____.*

5. **Star four precise topic words and check four high-utility academic words.**
   An example of a (precise topic word/high-utility academic word) is _____.

ASSESS A STUDENT SAMPLE

Read an additional student writing sample and rate it.

Scoring Guide			
1	Insufficient	3	Sufficient
2	Developing	4	Exemplary

1. Does the thesis statement clearly state the claim?	1	2	3	4
2. Do supporting paragraphs begin with a topic sentence that specifies a reason?	1	2	3	4
3. Did the writer give evidence drawn primarily from sources to support the claim?	1	2	3	4
4. Did the writer explain why the evidence is relevant and significant?	1	2	3	4
5. Did the writer use strong verbs to state and restate the claim?	1	2	3	4
6. Did the writer use transitions to introduce reasons and evidence?	1	2	3	4
7. Did the writer include precise topic words and high-utility words?	1	2	3	4
8. Does the conclusion statement strongly restate the claim using new wording?	1	2	3	4

REFLECT & REVISE

Record specific priorities and suggestions to help the writer.

The writer did an effective job of (organizing/including/stating) _____

_____

_____

One way the writer could make the justification essay stronger is _____

_____

_____

I noticed that the writer (forgot to/included/used) _____

_____

_____

This will support me with writing a justification essay because I will remember to

_____

_____

_____

Transitions to Introduce Evidence

Transitions	Examples
According to (source), _____. *In the text, (author's name) explains* _____. *The (source) points out* _____. *(Author's name) emphasizes* _____. *In addition, the text states* _____. *In my experience,* _____. *Based on my experience as a* _____. *Drawing from my experience as a* _____. *As an illustration,* _____.	**In the text, Jackson explains** that more than one-quarter of all vehicle crashes each year involved cell phone use. **The Center for Applied Linguistics points out** that more schools are offering courses in Arabic and Chinese. **In my experience,** lack of sleep has caused me to forget crucial test material. **As an illustration,** many people in my community are bilingual, which allows them to interact with more people.

IDENTIFY TRANSITIONS

Review the transitions that writers use to introduce evidence that supports a claim. Then complete each sentence below with an appropriate transition.

1. _____ only about one-third of teenagers feel they can use a credit card responsibly.

2. _____ that "credit repair clinics" charge steep fees and rarely help.

3. _____ teen with very little income, I am critically aware that credit cards can make overspending tempting.

WRITE SUPPORTING EVIDENCE

Write four sentences using transitions to introduce evidence that supports the claim.

1. _____

_____

_____

2. _____

_____

_____

3. _____

_____

_____

4. _____

_____

_____

Simple & Complex Sentences

Guidelines for Writing Simple & Complex Sentences

A **simple sentence** contains a subject and a predicate to express a complete thought.

A **complex sentence** contains a simple sentence and one or more dependent clauses.

A dependent clause cannot stand on its own as a sentence and often begins with a word such as *because*, *since*, or *that*.

Presenting Reasons	Examples
One reason I maintain this position is that _____.	**One reason I maintain this position is that** establishing good credit can make it easier to acquire an important loan later in life.
Another fundamental reason I hold this position is that _____.	**Another fundamental reason I hold this position is that** so many young people are getting themselves into serious debt.
Due to my own experience as (a/an) _____, I am critically aware that _____.	**Due to my own experience as** an impulsive shopper, **I am critically aware that** many teens cannot use credit cards responsibly.

Presenting Evidence	Examples
For instance, _____.	**For instance,** people with poor credit may only qualify for small, high-interest loans.
This is (important/significant) because _____.	**This is significant because** young people can quickly go from financial independence to debt.
Based on (current data/recent findings) that show _____, I maintain my position that _____.	**Based on current data that show** most teens don't understand how credit works, **I maintain my position that** teens should not be trusted with credit cards.

PRESENT REASONS & EVIDENCE

Write simple and complex sentences to present reasons and evidence.

Claim: Schools should start later to accommodate teens' sleep schedules.

Reason: One reason why I firmly believe that _____

is the fact that _____

Evidence: For instance, _____

_____

Claim: Schools _____ require students to study a foreign language.

Reason: A fundamental reason I hold this position is that _____

_____

so I am certain that _____

Evidence: This is important because _____

_____

Organize a Justification Essay

Prompt Are adolescents prepared to take on the responsibilities of using credit cards? Write a justification that states and supports your claim.

Thesis Starters	Examples
After analyzing the research on . . . After reviewing the (evidence/data) on . . . After examining the issues surrounding . . .	**After analyzing the research on** teens and driving, I strongly disagree that states should raise the driving age. **After reviewing the evidence on** vehicle crashes due to teen drivers, I am convinced that the driving age should be raised.
Conclusion Starters	**Examples**
For these reasons, In light of this evidence,	**For these reasons,** I conclude that a second language should be a requirement to graduate. **In light of this evidence,** I still maintain that students should not be required to study a foreign language to earn a diploma.

✏ WRITE A THESIS STATEMENT
Describe your claim.

My claim: _____

_____

Use academic language to restate your claim as a thesis statement.

_____ adolescents and financial responsibility,
(Thesis starter)

I (agree/disagree) _____ (strongly/firmly) _____

that _____
(your claim)

CHOOSE SUPPORTING TOPICS
List each topic you will write about to support your claim.

Supporting Paragraph 1

Topic: _____

_____

Supporting Paragraph 2

Topic: _____

_____

Supporting Paragraph 3

Topic: _____

_____

PLAN SUPPORTING PARAGRAPHS
List reasons and evidence that support your claim. You may draw from texts, your experience, or a classmate's experience.

Supporting Paragraph 1

Reason 1: _____

_____

Evidence: _____

_____

Source: _____

Author: _____

Elaboration on this evidence: _____

_____

_____

Supporting Paragraph 2

Reason 2: _____

_____

Evidence: _____

_____

Source: _____

Author: _____

Elaboration on this evidence: _____

_____

_____

Supporting Paragraph 3

Reason 3: _____

_____

Relevant personal experience: _____

_____

Relevant personal connection: _____

Elaboration on this evidence: _____

_____

_____

WRITE A CONCLUSION
Plan a conclusion statement that restates your claim.

_____ I contend that

(Conclusion starter)

_____

_____

Write a Justification Essay

Prompt Are adolescents prepared to take on the responsibilities of using credit cards? Write a justification that states and supports your claim.

 WRITE AN ESSAY

Use the frame to write your thesis statement, supporting paragraphs, and conclusion statement.

A

(Thesis starter)
_____
adolescents and financial responsibility, I (agree/disagree) _____

(strongly, firmly) _____ that _____
                                                      (claim)

_____

_____

_____

B1

One reason I maintain this position is _____
                                         (1st reason that supports your claim)

_____

_____

_____

In _____
    (title of source)
_____ presents (strong/convincing/compelling)
(author's name)

_____ (data/statistics/evidence) _____

regarding the (positive/negative/serious) _____ consequences

of _____
   (topic)

_____

_____

The author points out that _____
                            (text evidence)

_____

_____

This is significant because _____
                             (elaborate on text evidence)

_____

_____

_____

B2

Another (important/fundamental/critical) _____ reason I

hold this position is that _____

(2nd reason that supports your claim)

_____

_____

_____

According to _____

(source or author's name)

(text evidence)

_____

_____

This (data/evidence) _____ underscores (the need for/the

impact of/the seriousness of) _____

(elaborate on text evidence)

_____

_____

B3

In addition, my own relevant experience as _____

(relevant personal connection)

_____

has made me critically aware that _____

(claim)

_____

_____

_____

As an illustration, _____

(relevant personal experience)

_____

_____

_____

This is (evidence/proof) _____ that _____

(elaborate on personal experience)

_____

_____

_____

C

_____ I contend that

(Conclusion starter)

(restate your claim)

_____

_____

_____

60-Second Speech

IDENTIFY TOPIC

Choose one of the questions below to address in a 60-second speech.

☐ Should our state require teen drivers to display "new driver" decals on their cars?

☐ Should our school offer personal finance courses?

BRAINSTORM IDEAS

Write your position and two reasons that support it.

My Claim: _____

Reason 1: _____

Reason 2: _____

SYNTHESIZE IDEAS

Take notes on supporting evidence and a counterclaim.

Evidence 1: _____

_____

Evidence 2: _____

_____

Counterclaim: _____

_____

Response: _____

_____

WRITE A SPEECH

Write a 60-second speech that states your claim and includes reasons, evidence, and a counterclaim.

From my point of view, _____

_____

One reason is that _____

_____

Secondly, _____

_____

For example, _____

_____

Critics might claim that _____

_____

However, _____

_____

For these reasons, I _____ that _____

_____

Present & Rate Your Speech

Speaking at an Appropriate Pace

When presenting ideas during class or in a meeting, speak at an **appropriate pace**. Speak slowly, stop to breathe, and pause briefly to emphasize a point or to avoid inserting fillers such as *um, so,* or *like*.

PRESENT YOUR SPEECH

Present your speech to the small group. Make sure to speak at an appropriate pace.

LISTEN & TAKE NOTES

Listen attentively and take notes. Then indicate if you agree (+) or disagree (–).

> **Language to AFFIRM & CLARIFY**
>
> That's an intriguing perspective.
>
> I don't quite understand _____.

Classmate's Name	Idea	+/-

ASSESS YOUR SPEECH

Use the scoring guide to rate your speech.

Scoring Guide			
1	Insufficient	3	Sufficient
2	Developing	4	Exemplary

	1	2	3	4
1. Did your topic sentence clearly state your claim?	1	2	3	4
2. Did you include strong reasons and evidence to support your speech?	1	2	3	4
3. Did you include precise topic words?	1	2	3	4
4. Were you easy to understand?	1	2	3	4
5. Did you speak at an appropriate pace?	1	2	3	4

REFLECT

Think of two ways you can improve for your next speech.

Priority 1: I can strengthen my next speech by _____

_____

_____

Priority 2: In my next speech, I will include _____

_____

_____

When it comes to school, should teens plug in or opt out?

 BUILD KNOWLEDGE
Read and respond to the Data File (*Issues*, p. 70).

 BRAINSTORM IDEAS
Write a brief list of characteristics of online classes and traditional classes.

- online: can be taken at any time
-
-
-

 PRESENT IDEAS
Use the frames to discuss ideas with your group. Listen attentively and record the strongest ideas to complete the T-chart.

Language to FACILITATE DISCUSSION
So _____, what's your suggestion?
_____, what characteristics did you come up with?

1. The classes at a(n) (online/traditional) school _____ (**present-tense verb:** are available)

2. Another characteristic of (online/traditional) classes is that they _____ (**present-tense verb:** offer)

3. (Online/Traditional) classes also _____ (**present-tense verb:** follow)

4. One (advantage/drawback) to (online/traditional) classes is that they _____ (**present-tense verb:** lack)

ONLINE CLASSES	TRADITIONAL CLASSES
• can be taken from anywhere	• are only available at a set time

Words to Know

 BUILD WORD KNOWLEDGE

Rate your word knowledge. Then discuss word meanings and examples with your group.

	① Don't Know	② Recognize	③ Familiar	④ Know

Word to Know	Meaning	Examples
1 **digital** *adjective* ① ② ③ ④	involving the use of electronic or _____ technology	My dad is amazed by the high _____ _____ quality of the **digital** _____ produced today.
2 **individualized** *adjective* ① ② ③ ④	made to fit the special needs of a certain _____ _____	When my mother wanted to _____ _____ she took an **individualized** _____ _____ that was suited for her abilities.
3 **interactive** *adjective* ① ② ③ ④	when you can _____ with a computer system or program and have it react to your _____	**Interactive** _____ _____ are entertaining.
4 **access** *verb* ① ② ③ ④	to _____ information, especially on a _____	I use my smartphone to **access** _____
1 **discipline** *noun* ① ② ③ ④	the ability to _____ your own or someone else's behavior	It takes a great deal of **discipline** to stop _____ _____
2 **conventional** *adjective* ① ② ③ ④	around for a long time; considered to be _____ or _____	I get the news on _____ _____ rather than from **conventional** newspapers.
3 **virtual** *adjective* ① ② ③ ④	made, done, or seen on a _____ rather than in the _____	You can take a **virtual** tour of a _____ to help you decide if you want to _____ _____
4 **remedial** *adjective* ① ② ③ ④	meant to _____ _____ often for students who have difficulty _____ something	After one year in a **remedial** reading program, I was able to _____ _____ _____

Academic Discussion
Would you prefer to take courses online?

BRAINSTORM IDEAS

Briefly record at least two ideas in each column using everyday English.

Yes	No
• online study groups	• hard to make friends
•	•
•	•

ANALYZE WORDS

Complete the chart with precise words to discuss and write about the topic.

Everyday	Precise
easy *(adjective)*	comfortable,
alone *(adjective)*	lonely,
hold back *(verb)*	suppress,

MAKE A CLAIM

Rewrite two ideas using the frames and precise words.

Language to ELABORATE

To illustrate, _____.

I have observed that _____.

1. **Frame:** I (would/would not) prefer to take courses online because they _____ (**present-tense verb:** engage, allow, encourage)

   Response: _____

   _____

2. **Frame:** My preference is to (take/not take) courses online because I _____ (**present-tense verb:** learn, participate, interact)

   Response: _____

COLLABORATE

Listen attentively, restate, and record your partner's ideas.

Language to RESTATE

If I understand correctly, your opinion is that _____.

Yes, that's accurate.

Actually, what I (suggested/related) is that _____.

Classmate's Name	Ideas
	1.
	2.

Ten-Minute Paper

A **ten-minute paper** begins with a **claim**, followed by **two detail sentences** that elaborate with relevant examples and precise words.

 PRESENT IDEAS

Listen, compare ideas, and take notes. Then indicate if you agree (+) or disagree (–).

Classmate's Name	Idea	+/–

ELABORATE IN WRITING

Work with a partner to write a ten-minute paper.

I would not prefer to take courses online because they stifle students' curiosity. For example, students in traditional courses may feel more comfortable _____ _____ which may lead to _____ on related topics that are not part of the regular course material. As a result, the course material is _____ and all students are able to _____ from _____

Write a ten-minute paper.

My preference is to _____ courses online because I _____

For example, _____ _____

As a result, _____ _____

Words to Go

BUILD WORD KNOWLEDGE

Complete the meanings and examples for these high-utility academic words.

Words to Go	Meanings	Examples
accommodate ac·com·mo·date *verb*	to have enough _____ for a particular _____ of people or things	We are having our _____ in a _____ to **accommodate** the large number of attendees.
accommodation ac·com·mo·da·tion *noun*	a _____ for someone to _____ live, or work	I couldn't stay at _____ _____ because there were no **accommodations** for extra guests.

DISCUSS & WRITE EXAMPLES

Discuss your response with a partner. Then complete the sentence in writing.

Despite the fact that an SUV can **accommodate** many riders, it is safer for teens to _____

_____

Write your response and read it aloud to a partner.

At my sister's college, there are plenty of low-cost _____ for

students who need an affordable _____

BUILD WORD KNOWLEDGE

Complete the meanings and examples for these high-utility academic words.

Words to Go	Meanings	Examples
inclined in·clined *adjective*	_____ to do something or _____ a certain way	If I don't get enough _____ _____ I'm **inclined** to be cranky.
inclination in·cli·na·tion *noun*	a feeling that makes you _____ to do something	Because of _____ I haven't the slightest **inclination** to _____ _____ _____

DISCUSS & WRITE EXAMPLES

Discuss your response with a partner. Then complete the sentence in writing.

Victims of bullying are often **inclined** not to _____

_____ because they want to avoid further incidents.

Write your response and read it aloud to a partner.

My _____ is to spend money as soon as I get it, even though I

know that _____ is the responsible thing to do.

Close Reading

BUILD FLUENCY
Read the text "Cyber Students" (*Issues*, pp. 71–73).

IDENTIFY KEY IDEAS & DETAILS
Take turns asking and answering questions with a partner. Then write brief notes.

Discussion Frames	Text Notes
Q: What is the text **primarily about**? **A:** The text is **primarily about** _____.	• arguments supporting and opposing _____ _____
Q: What are the **most important details** in this text? **A:** One **essential detail** in this text is _____. **A:** An additional **essential detail** in this text is _____.	• proponents: online classes _____; critics: lack of _____ harmful • Birkenes: good prep for _____; _____ lessons; _____ • Brown: students won't learn _____ _____; requires _____

RESPOND WITH EVIDENCE
Use the frames and evidence from the text to construct formal written responses.

1. According to the text, what are one pro and one con of taking online courses?

   According to the text, _____ is one pro of taking online courses.

   One con is the lack of _____

   _____

Use the frame to analyze Dontaé Brown's point of view.

2. What is the effect of Dontaé Brown's question at the end of the first paragraph in the section "Power Down"? What does it tell us about his point of view?

   By asking the question, Dontaé is suggesting that the idea of students willingly cutting

   back their online social activities is _____

   It tells readers that the author has a _____

   point of view toward the way students prefer to use their online time.

IDENTIFY PRECISE WORDS
Review Text 1 and your *Portfolio* (pp. 150–155) to identify words for your writing.

Topic Words	High-Utility Academic Words
• online credits	• adept
•	•
•	•

Academic Discussion
HOW ARE CONVENTIONAL SCHOOLS AND VIRTUAL SCHOOLS DIFFERENT?

 BRAINSTORM IDEAS

Briefly record at least two ideas in each column using everyday English.

Conventional Schools	Virtual Schools
• take notes by hand	• can.be accessed from anywhere
•	•
•	•

 ANALYZE WORDS

Complete the chart with precise words to discuss and write about the issue.

Everyday	Precise
grab *(verb)*	engage,
move *(verb)*	motivate,
carry *(verb)*	convey,

 MAKE A CLAIM

Rewrite two ideas using the frames and precise words. Then prepare to elaborate verbally.

> **Language to ELABORATE**
>
> To illustrate, _____.
>
> I have observed that _____.

1. **Frame:** Conventional and virtual schools are different in terms of their _____ (**noun:** course offerings, class sizes, cost)

    Response: _____

    _____

2. **Frame:** Virtual schools _____ (**present-tense verb:** prepare, offer, save), while conventional schools _____ (**present-tense verb:** lack, individualize, cost)

    Response: _____

    _____

COLLABORATE

Listen attentively, restate, and record your partner's ideas.

> **Language to RESTATE**
>
> If I understand correctly, your opinion is that _____.
>
> Yes, that's accurate.
>
> Actually, what I (suggested/related) is that _____.

Classmate's Name	Ideas
	1.
	2.

Ten-Minute Paper

A **ten-minute** paper begins with a **claim,** followed by **two detail sentences** that elaborate with relevant examples and precise words.

Language to COMPARE IDEAS

My opinion is (similar to/different from) _____'s.

PRESENT IDEAS

Listen, compare ideas, and take notes. Then indicate if you agree (+) or disagree (–).

Classmate's Name	Idea	+/–

ELABORATE IN WRITING

Work with a partner to write a ten-minute paper.

Language to COLLABORATE

What should we write?

We could choose _____. What do you think is a strong choice?

In addition, we could write _____.

Conventional and virtual schools are different in terms of their ability to accommodate different class sizes. For example, students can attend a _____ _____ from just about anywhere by using _____ and _____ As a result, virtual schools can _____ many more students per class than a _____ because they aren't restricted by the _____ of a classroom.

Write a ten-minute paper.

Virtual schools _____

while conventional schools _____

_____ For example, _____

_____

_____

As a result, _____

_____

_____

Words to Go

 BUILD WORD KNOWLEDGE

Complete the meaning and examples for this high-utility academic word.

Word to Go	Meaning	Examples
comparable com·pa·ra·ble *adjective*	similar to something else in _____ _____ _____ etc.	I'm a decent _____ but I'm not **comparable** to someone like _____ My parents complimented me by saying _____ _____ was **comparable** to that of a professional.

DISCUSS & WRITE EXAMPLES

Discuss your response with a partner. Then complete the sentence in writing.

The _____ at my school are good,

but they aren't **comparable** to _____

Write your response and read it aloud to a partner.

I firmly believe that _____

is a _____ crime to physical bullying.

 BUILD WORD KNOWLEDGE

Complete the meanings and examples for these high-utility academic words.

Words to Go	Meanings	Examples
estimate es·ti·mate *noun*	a rough _____ about an amount, distance, value, or other quantity	I don't know exactly how much _____ _____ I'll need for _____ _____ but I can give you a good **estimate**.
estimated es·ti·mat·ed *adjective*	roughly _____ in a way that is not _____	An **estimated** 200 _____ _____ are coming to _____ _____ next month.

DISCUSS & WRITE EXAMPLES

Discuss your response with a partner. Then complete the sentence in writing.

I'm not entirely sure how many _____.

but I would **estimate** _____

Write your response and read it aloud to a partner.

An _____ 300 students showed up to school on Saturday to _____

_____

Section Shrink

 BUILD FLUENCY

Read the introduction and Section 1 of the text "More Pupils Are Learning Online, Fueling Debate on Quality" (*Issues*, pp. 74–76).

 IDENTIFY KEY IDEAS & DETAILS

Take turns asking and answering questions with a partner. Then write brief notes.

Discussion Frames	Text Notes
Q: What does this section **focus on**? A: This section **focuses on** _____.	• online classes save _____ but may not _____ well
Q: What are the **significant details** in this section? A: (One/An additional) **significant detail** in this section is _____. A: Perhaps the **most significant detail** in this section is _____.	• online courses _____ to prep students for _____ • online courses _____ but unsure if students _____ • schools can offer _____ and _____ online classes; allows _____ be taught

 SUMMARIZE

"Shrink" Section 1 of the text by writing a summary in 40 or fewer words.

CLASS SUMMARY   **WORD COUNT:** _____

Several states offer online courses to provide _____ and

_____ or to accommodate _____

in schools with _____ but critics say the

real motive is _____

and that the courses _____ students.

PARTNER SUMMARY   **WORD COUNT:** _____

Some states require students to take online courses as _____

for _____ while others provide courses to

accommodate _____ or to make

_____ available, but skeptics believe such

courses _____ school budgets, not _____

Q **IDENTIFY PRECISE WORDS**

Review Section 1 and your *Portfolio* (pp. 156–159) to identify words for your writing.

Topic Words	High-Utility Academic Words
• online programs	• increasingly
•	•
•	•

Words to Go

BUILD WORD KNOWLEDGE
Complete the meanings and examples for these high-utility academic words.

Words to Go	Meanings	Examples
effective ef·fec·tive *adjective*	having the intended _____	_____ _____ is an **effective** way to lose weight.
effectiveness ef·fec·tive·ness *noun*	power to bring about the intended result; _____	I doubted the **effectiveness** of begging my parents to let me _____ _____ but they actually agreed.

DISCUSS & WRITE EXAMPLES
Discuss your response with a partner. Then complete the sentence in writing.

Turning off _____ early in

the evening can be very **effective** when trying to get a good night's sleep.

Write your response and read it aloud to a partner.

It is hard to question the _____ of getting a good night's sleep,

when it consistently leads to _____

BUILD WORD KNOWLEDGE
Complete the meanings and examples for these high-utility academic words.

Words to Go	Meanings	Examples
attribute at·trib·ute *verb*	to give someone or something _____ for something	I **attribute** my _____ _____ skills to years of practice.
attributable at·trib·u·ta·ble *adjective*	likely to have been _____ by something	The absence of so many students was **attributable** to _____ _____

DISCUSS & WRITE EXAMPLES
Discuss your response with a partner. Then complete the sentence in writing.

I **attributed** the anxiety I felt before the test to _____

_____

Write your response and read it aloud to a partner.

A high percentage of traffic deaths are _____ to _____

_____

Section Shrink

 BUILD FLUENCY
Read Section 2 of "More Pupils Are Learning Online, Fueling Debate on Quality" (*Issues*, pp. 76–78).

 IDENTIFY KEY IDEAS & DETAILS
Take turns asking and answering questions with a partner. Then write brief notes.

Discussion Frames	Text Notes
Q: What does this section **focus on**? **A:** This section **focuses on** _____.	• growth of online _____ _____ courses
Q: What are the **significant details** in this section? **A:** (One/An additional) **significant detail** in this section is _____. **A:** Perhaps the **most significant detail** in this section is _____.	• number of online courses growing, but little _____ to show effectiveness for _____ • _____ courses criticized for artificially boosting graduation rates • _____ is a problem among students in online courses

 SUMMARIZE
"Shrink" Section 2 of the text by writing a summary in 40 or fewer words.

CLASS SUMMARY   **WORD COUNT:** _____

The lack of _____ that online courses benefit K–12 students

hasn't curtailed their _____ especially

_____ courses, which have been

blamed for fraudulently improving _____ by

allowing _____ and often _____ students to pass.

PARTNER SUMMARY   **WORD COUNT:** _____

Critics say _____ haven't been proven to benefit

_____ and credit recovery courses encourage

_____ and allow _____

to pass just so schools can _____ their student graduation rates.

 IDENTIFY PRECISE WORDS
Review Section 2 and your *Portfolio* (pp. 160–161) to identify words for your writing.

Topic Words	High-Utility Academic Words
• credit recovery	• appeal
•	•
•	•

Words to Go

 BUILD WORD KNOWLEDGE

Complete the meanings and examples for these high-utility academic words.

Words to Go	Meanings	Examples
enhance en·hance *verb*	to _____ something	I hoped _____ would **enhance** my mood, but it only made me _____
enhanced en·hanced *adjective*	_____ or better	The **enhanced** features on my new smart phone include _____ _____

 DISCUSS & WRITE EXAMPLES

Discuss your response with a partner. Then complete the sentence in writing.

Steroids can **enhance** an athlete's performance, but they are _____

_____

Write your response and read it aloud to a partner.

The _____ images of athletes in sports magazines cause many

teenagers to _____ by comparison.

 BUILD WORD KNOWLEDGE

Complete the meanings and examples for these high-utility academic words.

Words to Go	Meanings	Examples
mandate man·date *noun*	an official _____ to do something	The principal issued a **mandate** that all students must _____ _____ _____
mandate man·date *verb*	to officially _____ something to be done	My brother's college plans to **mandate** ___ _____ _____

 DISCUSS & WRITE EXAMPLES

Discuss your response with a partner. Then complete the sentence in writing.

Our school received a **mandate** from the district to _____

_____

Write your response and read it aloud to a partner.

Last year, a school that _____ random drug tests was sued on the

grounds that the rule was _____

Section Shrink

 BUILD FLUENCY

Read Section 3 of "More Pupils Are Learning Online, Fueling Debate on Quality" (*Issues*, pp. 78–80).

 IDENTIFY KEY IDEAS & DETAILS

Take turns asking and answering questions with a partner. Then write brief notes.

Discussion Frames	Text Notes
Q: What does this section **focus on**? **A:** This section **focuses on** _____.	• _____ and _____ debate surrounding online courses
Q: What are the **significant details** in this section? **A:** (One/An additional) **significant detail** in this section is _____. **A:** Perhaps the **most significant detail** in this section is _____.	• administrators claim _____ _____ the reason for online courses, not _____ • conservative groups support _____ _____ schools; accused of replacing _____ with _____ • _____ push for online courses, but _____ say only _____ benefit

 SUMMARIZE

"Shrink" Section 3 of the text by writing a summary in 40 or fewer words.

CLASS SUMMARY   **WORD COUNT:** _____

Proponents of online courses claim they are intended to _____ _____ especially for those with _____ but critics say they take away _____ and serve to make _____ wealthy.

PARTNER SUMMARY   **WORD COUNT:** _____

Supporters of online courses proclaim their _____ merit and deny that _____ and _____ are motives for promoting them, while opponents _____ online courses because they _____ teaching jobs and _____ corporations.

IDENTIFY PRECISE WORDS

Review Section 3 and your *Portfolio* (pp. 162–163) to identify words for your writing.

Topic Words	High-Utility Academic Words
• administrators	• devote
•	•
•	•

Student Writing Model

Academic Writing Type

A **formal written summary** provides an objective overview of the topic and important details from an informational text. The writer credits the author, but writes in primarily his or her own words, without including personal opinions.

   A. The **topic sentence** includes the text type, title, author, and topic.
   B. **Detail sentences** include the important details from the summarized text.
   C. The **concluding sentence** restates the author's conclusion in the writer's own words.

ANALYZE TEXT

Read this student model to analyze the elements of a formal summary.

A

   In the opinion article titled "Cyber Students," Adele Birkenes argues that students should be required to take online courses. Birkenes begins by pointing out that students are naturally inclined to spend much of their time in the digital world, so it is only logical to have them use some of that time to earn school credit. The author continues to report that online courses are common in colleges, so requiring students to take them in high school is effective

B

preparation for college and even the modern-day workplace. She describes further how interactive videos and an abundance of resources unavailable in conventional classrooms improve the learning experience. Moreover, the author discusses the accessibility of virtual classes that can be taken from any location with an Internet connection. Birkenes concludes by emphasizing that

C

online courses can accommodate a range of students by allowing them to learn as quickly or as slowly as they need.

MARK & DISCUSS ELEMENTS

Mark the summary elements and use the frames to discuss them with your partner.

1. **Number (1–4) the four elements of the topic sentence.**
   The topic sentence includes the _____.

2. **Draw a box around four transition words or phrases.**
   One transition (word/phrase) is _____.

3. **Underline four important details.** *One important detail in this summary is* _____.

4. **Circle four citation verbs.** *One citation verb that the writer uses is* _____.

5. **Star four precise topic words and check four high-utility academic words.**
   An example of a (precise topic word/high-utility academic word) is _____.

Organize a Formal Summary

Prompt	Write a formal summary of "More Pupils Are Learning Online, Fueling Debate on Quality."

Guidelines for Paraphrasing Multiple Sentences

Paraphrase related details from a source text by combining key information into one sentence. Replace key words and phrases with synonyms and keep important topic words.

Text Detail 1	Text Detail 2	Text Detail 3
"… [Officials] want to give students skills they will need in college, where online courses are increasingly common, and in the 21st-century workplace" (Gabriel 75).	"In New York, Innovation Zone, or iZone, includes online makeup and Advanced Placement courses at 30 high schools …" (Gabriel 76).	"… [Superintendent Reza Namin] could not justify continuing to pay a Chinese-language teacher for only 10 interested students" (Gabriel 76).

PARAPHRASE IDEAS

Combine key information from the three text details above into one detail sentence.

States offer online courses for several reasons, which can include providing

(Text Detail 1) _____

(Text Detail 2) _____ and

(Text Detail 3) _____

PLAN KEY IDEAS & DETAILS

State the text information to write a topic sentence.

In the news article titled (title) _____

(author's full name) _____ (citation verb: examines, discusses)

_____ (topic) _____

List four important details from the article primarily using your own words.

1. _____

_____

2. _____

_____

3. _____

_____

4. _____

Restate the author's conclusion in your own words.

_____

_____

Write a Formal Summary

Prompt | Write a formal summary of "More Pupils Are Learning Online, Fueling Debate on Quality."

✏️ WRITE A PARAGRAPH

Use the frame to write your topic sentence, detail sentences, and concluding sentence.

A

In the _____ titled _____
(text type)   (title)

_____   _____
(author's full name)   (present-tense citation verb)

_____
(topic)

_____

_____

B

_____ begins by _____
(Author's last name)   (citation verb + -ing: presenting, arguing)

_____
(1st important detail)

_____

_____

_____

The (author/writer/researcher) _____ continues to _____
                                                                  (citation verb, base form: describe, report)

_____
(2nd important detail)

_____

_____

_____

(He/She) _____ _____ further that _____
                          (present-tense citation verb)

_____
(3rd important detail)

_____

_____

_____

Moreover, the (author/writer/researcher) _____
                                           (present-tense citation verb)

_____
(4th important detail)

_____

_____

_____

C

_____ concludes by _____
(Author's last name)   (citation verb + -ing: suggesting, emphasizing)

_____
(restate author's conclusion)

_____

Rate Your Summary

 ASSESS YOUR DRAFT

Rate your formal summary. Then have your partner rate it.

Scoring Guide	
1	Insufficient
2	Developing
3	Sufficient
4	Exemplary

1. Does the topic sentence state the title, author, and topic?	Self	1	2	3	4
	Partner	1	2	3	4
2. Did you paraphrase the most important details from the text?	Self	1	2	3	4
	Partner	1	2	3	4
3. Did you use citation verbs to credit the author?	Self	1	2	3	4
	Partner	1	2	3	4
4. Did you use transitions to introduce and sequence details?	Self	1	2	3	4
	Partner	1	2	3	4
5. Did you include precise topic words and high-utility academic words?	Self	1	2	3	4
	Partner	1	2	3	4
6. Did you restate the author's conclusion using your own words?	Self	1	2	3	4
	Partner	1	2	3	4

 REFLECT & REVISE

Record specific priorities and suggestions to help you and your partner revise.

(Partner) Positive Feedback: I appreciate how you (used/included) _____

_____

_____

(Partner) Suggestion: As you revise your summary, focus on _____

_____

_____

(Self) Priority 1: My summary paragraph needs _____

_____

_____

(Self) Priority 2: I plan to improve my summary by _____

_____

_____

CHECK & EDIT

Use this checklist to proofread and edit your summary.

☐ Did you capitalize the title of the news article and proper nouns?

☐ Did you put quotation marks around the title of the article?

☐ Did you use commas appropriately after transitions?

☐ Do simple present-tense verbs end in –s?

☐ Is each sentence complete?

☐ Are all words spelled correctly?

Words to Know

 BUILD WORD KNOWLEDGE

Rate your word knowledge. Then discuss word meanings and examples with your group.

		① Don't Know	② Recognize	③ Familiar	④ Know

Word to Know	Meaning	Examples
1 **reality** *noun*	what actually happens or is _____ not what is _____ or thought	I've been accused of being _____ _____ but the **reality** is I'm shy. I love to _____ _____ as an escape from **reality**.
2 **anonymity** *noun*	when other people do not know _____ _____ or what your name is	The _____ _____ I wore to the party gave me **anonymity**. In order to comment on the blog with **anonymity**, I _____ _____
3 **differentiate** *verb*	to identify ways in which two or more things or people are _____ _____	Identical twins may _____ _____ so people can **differentiate** between them. My baby brother still can't **differentiate** between _____ _____
4 **contributing** *adjective*	_____ to make something happen	_____ _____ was a **contributing** part of my failure to remember what I had studied the night before. Stress is a **contributing** factor of _____ _____

Close Reading

 READ THE TEXT
Read an excerpt from *Ready Player One* (*Issues*, pp. 81–87).

 IDENTIFY KEY IDEAS & DETAILS

Making Inferences

To make an **inference**, the reader combines various facts and points of information from the text with his or her own prior knowledge to figure out something the author has not explicitly stated.

Use the frames to analyze the text and make inferences.

1. What inference can you make about the state of the real world outside the OASIS based on the author's use of the phrase "in these dark times" on page 81?

   Based on the author's use of the phrase "in these dark times," I can infer _____

   _____

   _____

2. What inferences can you make based on Wade3's encounter with Todd13?

   When Wade3 retorts, or responds to, Todd13's insults, he never even _____

   _____

   This reveals that Wade3 _____

   _____

 ANALYZE CRAFT & STRUCTURE

Analyzing Figurative Language

Authors use **figurative language**, words and phrases with a meaning that is different from their literal interpretation, to help the reader visualize what is happening.

Use the frames to analyze the author's use of figurative language.

3. Wade3 says "I nearly broke my neck sprinting to the office to submit my application" for OASIS's public schools. What does the figurative language "nearly broke my neck" emphasize about Wade3's desire to attend school in the OASIS?

   The author uses the figurative language _____

   to emphasize that Wade3 _____

   _____

What does Wade3 mean when he says, "At this school, the only real weapons are words"?

   Since _____ is forbidden on Ludus, the only way students can

   _____ one another is by _____

   _____

Academic Discussion

What are the potential advantages and disadvantages of attending a virtual school?

 BRAINSTORM IDEAS

Briefly record at least two ideas in each column using everyday English.

Advantages	Disadvantages
• no bullies	• missing out on socializing
•	•
•	•

 ANALYZE WORDS

Complete the chart with precise words to discuss and write about the topic.

Everyday	Precise
hide *(verb)*	camouflage,
copy *(verb)*	plagiarize,
disrespect *(noun)*	indignity,

 MAKE A CLAIM

Rewrite two ideas using the frames and precise words. Then prepare to elaborate verbally.

Language to ELABORATE
To illustrate, _____.
I have observed that _____.

1. **Frame:** One potential (advantage/disadvantage) of attending a virtual school is _____ (**verb + –ing:** accessing, earning, socializing with)

   Response: _____

   _____

2. **Frame:** A potential (advantage/disadvantage) of attending a virtual school is that students may _____ (**base verb:** plagiarize, remain, participate)

   Response: _____

   _____

COLLABORATE

Listen attentively, restate, and record your partner's ideas.

Language to RESTATE
If I understand correctly, your opinion is that _____.
Yes, that's accurate.
Actually, what I (suggested/related) is that _____.

Classmate's Name	Ideas
	1.
	2.

Ten-Minute Paper

A **ten-minute paper** begins with a **claim,** followed by **two detail sentences** that elaborate with relevant examples and precise words.

Language to COMPARE IDEAS

My opinion is (similar to/different from) _____'s.

PRESENT IDEAS

Listen, compare ideas, and take notes. Then indicate if you agree (+) or disagree (–).

Classmate's Name	Idea	+/–

ELABORATE IN WRITING

Work with the teacher to write a ten-minute paper.

Language to COLLABORATE

What should we write?

We could choose _____. What do you think is a strong choice?

In addition, we could write _____.

A potential disadvantage of attending a virtual school is that students may plagiarize. For example, a student may need to answer questions about a _____ _____ he or she was supposed _____ but didn't.

As a result, the student can _____

by looking up _____

about the book online, _____

the answers, and submit the work as his or her _____

Work with a partner to write a ten-minute paper.

A potential _____ of attending a virtual school is that students

may _____

For example, _____

_____

_____

As a result, _____

_____

_____

Take a Stand

Debate Should states mandate that students take online courses?

 COLLABORATE
Read the debate question about online learning. Then take turns using a frame to respond with your initial reaction.

ANALYZE SOURCES
Read a quote that either supports or opposes the debate topic. Then paraphrase.

Language to RESPOND

So _____, what is your initial reaction?

My initial reaction is _____.

_____ and I had (similar/somewhat different) initial reactions.

Quote	Paraphrase
Model: "[Critics] worry that the online classes do not serve the needs of the students who need individualized attention" (Birkenes and Brown 71).	To put it another way, critics think that students requiring _____ time with teachers _____ _____ in online courses.
1. "A recent survey published by the Sloan Consortium showed that 31 percent of students in college take at least one course online" (Birkenes 72).	This quote clarifies that it is _____ _____ for _____ _____ to offer _____ _____
2. "'Many high school students have not developed the skill set necessary to be successful in this type of learning'" (Brown 73).	To put it another way, online courses require certain _____ that high school students might _____ _____
3. "Officials for Memphis City Schools say they want to give students skills they will need in college, where online courses are increasingly common, and in the 21st-century workplace" (Gabriel 75).	To put it another way, the goal of _____ to take online courses is to provide them with the _____ they need to do well in _____ and _____
4. "[The United States Department of Education] found benefits in online courses for college students, but it concluded that few rigorous studies had been done at the K-12 level, and policy makers 'lack scientific evidence of the effectiveness' of online classes" (Gabriel 77).	This quote clarifies that there hasn't been _____ to prove that online courses actually _____ _____

Debate Ideas

SYNTHESIZE IDEAS

Write a response to the debate question, including a paraphrase of a text quote and elaboration on the quote.

Claim: My position is that states (should/should not) _____

mandate that students take online courses.

Transition Statement: I have (one key reason/a compelling reason) _____

_____ for taking this stance.

Quote Paraphrase: (For example,/According to (author),) _____.

_____

_____

_____

Quote Elaboration: (As a result,/Consequently,) _____.

_____

_____

_____

PRESENT EVIDENCE

Maintaining a Confident Posture

When presenting ideas during class or in a meeting, maintain a **confident posture.** Take a deep breath before speaking, stand up straight, and face your audience.

LISTEN & TAKE NOTES

Listen attentively and take notes.
Then indicate if you agree (+) or disagree (–).

Language to AFFIRM & CLARIFY

I hadn't thought of that.
What do you mean by _____ ?

Classmate's Name	Idea	+/-

Student Writing Model

Academic Writing Type

An **argument** states a claim and supports it with logical reasons and relevant evidence from sources.

> **A.** The **thesis statement** clearly states the writer's claim and tells what the writer will explain about the topic.
>
> **B.** **Supporting paragraphs** support the claim with reasons and evidence from sources. The writer also presents counterclaims and responds with strong evidence.
>
> **C.** The **conclusion statement** restates the writer's claim about the issue.

 ANALYZE TEXT

Read this student model to analyze elements of an argument research paper.

A
After examining the issues surrounding online learning, I am convinced that states should require students to attend digital classes.

B
One reason I maintain this position is that online courses will ensure that students will be able to take classes required for graduation, despite a lack of teachers. In "More Pupils Are Learning Online, Fueling Debate on Quality," Trip Gabriel presents strong data regarding the positive consequences of virtual courses. For example, Miami schools would have failed to accommodate all students due to a lack of teachers, but 7,000 high school students were able to access necessary course materials via online courses (Gabriel 76). Opponents of online courses tend to highlight that the quality of the education isn't comparable to that offered in conventional schools. However, current data actually demonstrate that the research on the effectiveness of online courses is inadequate in order to back up that claim.

I am also in favor of state-mandated online courses due to the benefits they provide students. Adele Birkenes emphasizes in "Cyber Students" that online courses prepare students for college and the 21st century workplace (72). One particularly compelling statistic is that an estimated one-third of all college students take a minimum of one online course (Birkenes 72).

C
Whether states mandate that students should take online courses will remain a controversial issue. After reviewing relevant data, I contend that states should require online courses for students.

MARK & DISCUSS ELEMENTS

Mark the argument elements and use the frames to discuss them with your partner.

1. **Circle the writer's claim within the thesis statement.**
   The writer's claim is _____.

2. **Underline and label two reasons that support the writer's claim with the letter *R*.**
   One reason that supports the writer's claim is _____.

3. **Underline and label four pieces of evidence that support the writer's claim with the letter *E*.** *One piece of evidence that supports the writer's claim is _____.*

4. **Draw a box around a counterclaim.** *One counterclaim is _____.*

5. **Star four precise topic words and check four high-utility academic words.**
   An example of a (precise topic word/high-utility academic word) is _____.

ASSESS A STUDENT SAMPLE

Read an additional student writing sample and rate it.

Scoring Guide	
1	Insufficient
2	Developing
3	Sufficient
4	Exemplary

1. Does the thesis statement clearly state the claim?	1	2	3	4
2. Do supporting paragraphs begin with a topic sentence that specifies a reason?	1	2	3	4
3. Did the writer give evidence drawn primarily from sources to support the claim?	1	2	3	4
4. Did the writer explain why the evidence is relevant and significant?	1	2	3	4
5. Did the writer include complex sentences to present and respond to counterclaims?	1	2	3	4
6. Did the writer use strong verbs and verb phrases to express opinions?	1	2	3	4
7. Did the writer use transitions to introduce reasons and evidence?	1	2	3	4
8. Did the writer use precise adjectives to describe evidence?	1	2	3	4
9. Did the writer include citation information for text evidence?	1	2	3	4
10. Did the writer include precise topic words and high-utility words?	1	2	3	4
11. Does the conclusion statement strongly restate the claim using new wording?	1	2	3	4

REFLECT & REVISE

Record specific priorities and suggestions to help the writer.

The writer did an effective job of (organizing/including/stating) _____

_____

_____

One way the writer could make the argument stronger is _____

_____

_____

I noticed that the writer (forgot to/included/used) _____

_____

_____

This will support me with writing an argument because I will remember to _____

_____

_____

Paraphrasing Text

Guidelines for Paraphrasing Text

Look for text evidence that supports your position. Then **paraphrase** it by replacing key words and phrases with precise synonyms and your own words. Remember to keep important topic words in your paraphrase.

Source Text	Key Words & Phrases → Precise Synonyms			Paraphrasing
"Online courses open up a student to a variety of resources that they might not have available in the classroom" (Birkenes 72).	online courses	→	virtual classes	Virtual classes offer students diverse resources not limited to those in a classroom.
	open up a student to	→	offer students	
	a variety of	→	diverse	
	not have available	→	not limited to	

⊕ IDENTIFY PRECISE SYNONYMS

Read these statements and replace the words in parentheses with precise synonyms.

1. In the 2011–2012 school year, (*over 2,500,000*) _____ students took (*at least*) _____ one online course.

2. Five states now (*require*) _____ that students take online courses (*in order to graduate*) _____

3. The number of K–12 students (*taking part*) _____ in full-time online public school has (*risen*) _____ 450% over the past five years.

4. (*Supporters*) _____ of the laws say that online classes help (*train*) _____ students for the digital world.

✎ PARAPHRASE IDEAS

Paraphrase the four statements above using your own words and phrasing.

1. Recent surveys show that _____
_____
_____

2. The latest findings indicate that _____
_____
_____

3. Statistics show that _____
_____
_____

4. For example, _____
_____
_____

Conditional Verbs

Guidelines for Using Conditional Verbs

Conditional verbs describe what might or could happen. They show what conditions would be like if a recommendation became reality.

A real future possibility: will, shall, can, may (+ base verb)

Requiring students to take online courses can save school districts money.

An uncertain future possibility: would, should, could, might (+ base verb)

If online courses continue to grow in popularity, plagiarism could become a serious issue.

A past impossibility: would have, should have, could have, might have (+ past participle)

Before credit recovery courses existed, failing students would have had to repeat a grade.

 IDENTIFY CONDITIONAL VERBS

Read the argument and circle the conditional verbs.

> After examining the issues surrounding cheating in online courses, I believe that virtual schools should implement stricter anti-cheating measures. One reason I maintain this position is that students will continue to try to find ways to beat the system. In "Are They Learning or Cheating? Online Teaching's Dilemma," George Anders presents compelling data regarding the negative consequences of not detecting cheating students. For example, students can create fake online identities that enable them to take a course over and over until they memorize the test answers. Students who might have failed an exam could pass without ever learning the material. Whether online schools can stop cheating will remain a controversial issue. After reviewing recent data, I conclude that they should at least try.

 WRITE CONDITIONAL VERBS

Use a conditional verb to complete each sentence.

1. Requiring students to spend even more time online than they already do _____

   _____

2. If more states had mandated online classes last year, _____

   _____

3. Officials for Memphis City Schools claim that online courses _____

   _____

4. Continuing budget cuts _____

   _____

Organize an Argument

Prompt | Should states mandate that students take online courses? Write an argument that states your claim and supports it with text evidence.

Guidelines for Crediting an Author

Paraphrase significant blocks of text evidence to avoid having too many quotes and to maintain your own voice in the argument. Credit the author when you paraphrase to avoid plagiarizing and to show that your argument is valid and supported by an authority.

Source Text	Paraphrased Idea
"School is the place where we learn to interact with one another. School is where we learn to hold meaningful discussions and to read one another's body language and facial expressions. Online classes defeat that purpose" (Brown 73).	Conventional schools, unlike virtual schools, are where students traditionally learn important social skills, such as interacting with others, the art of conversation, and picking up physical cues like gestures and facial expressions (Brown 73).

WRITE A THESIS STATEMENT
Describe your claim.

My claim: _____

_____

Use academic language to restate your claim as a thesis statement.

_____ online learning

(Thesis starter)

I (agree/disagree) _____ (strongly/firmly) _____

_____

(your claim)

_____

CHOOSE SUPPORTING TOPICS
List each topic you will write about to support your claim.

Supporting Paragraph 1

Topic: _____

_____

Supporting Paragraph 2

Topic: _____

_____

PLAN SUPPORTING PARAGRAPHS
List reasons and text evidence that support your claim. Include a counterclaim and a response supported with strong evidence.

Supporting Paragraph 1:

Reason 1: _____

_____

Evidence: _____

_____

Source: _____

Author: _____

Counterclaim: _____

_____

Response to counterclaim: _____

_____

Source: _____

Author: _____

Supporting Paragraph 2:

Reason 2: _____

_____

Evidence: _____

_____

_____

Source: _____

Author: _____

Statistical Evidence: _____

_____

_____

Source: _____

WRITE A CONCLUSION
Plan a conclusion that restates your claim.

Whether _____
      _(restate the issue)

will remain a controversial issue. After reviewing (recent/relevant/substantial)

_____ data, I _____ that _____
                              (verb/verb phrase to express opinion)   (restate your claim)

_____

Write an Argument

Prompt | Should states mandate that students take online courses? Write an argument that states your claim and supports it with text evidence.

 WRITE A RESEARCH PAPER
Use the frame to write your thesis statement, supporting paragraphs, and conclusion statement.

A

_____
(Thesis starter)

_____
(topic)

I _____
(verb/verb phrase to express opinion)

that _____
(strongly state your claim)

B1

One reason I maintain this position is that _____
(1st reason that supports your claim)

_____

_____

In _____
(title of source)

_____ presents (convincing/strong) _____
(author's full name)

data regarding the (positive/negative) _____ consequences of

_____
(topic)

_____

For example, _____
(evidence from source)

_____

_____

(Opponents/Proponents) _____ of _____
(topic)

tend to (emphasize/point out/highlight) _____
(counterclaim)

_____

However, (current data/studies) _____ actually demonstrate

that _____
(your response to counterclaim)

_____

B2

I am also (in favor of/opposed to) _____ _____
(topic)

_____

due to _____
(2nd reason that supports your claim)

_____

_____

_____

_____ emphasizes in _____
(Author's full name)   (title of source)

that _____
(evidence from a different source)

_____

_____

_____

One particularly (convincing/alarming/compelling) _____

statistic is _____
(statistic from a source)

_____

_____

_____

_____

_____

C

Whether _____
(restate the issue)

_____

will remain a controversial issue. After reviewing (recent/relevant/substantial)

_____ data, I _____ that
(verb/verb phrase to express opinion)

_____
(restate your claim)

_____

_____

ARE TEENS READY TO GET TO WORK?

BUILD KNOWLEDGE
Read and respond to the Data File (*Issues,* p. 88).

BRAINSTORM IDEAS
Write a brief list of what can help teens prepare for a good career.

- responsibility
-
-
-

PRESENT IDEAS
Use the frames to discuss ideas with your group. Listen attentively and record the strongest ideas to complete the organizer.

Language to FACILITATE DISCUSSION
So, _____, what's your point of view?
_____, what example did you come up with?

1. A teen looking for a good career should _____ (**present-tense verb:** develop)

2. In school, a teen concerned about work should _____ (**present-tense verb:** strive for)

3. Teens will be well positioned for careers if they _____ (**present-tense verb:** obtain)

4. Teens' career plans could also _____ (**present-tense verb:** include)

CAREER DEVELOPMENT

PERSONAL
- dedication
-
-
-

ACADEMIC
- excellence in school
-
-
-

OTHER
- connections in business
-
-

Words to Know

 BUILD WORD KNOWLEDGE

Rate your word knowledge. Then discuss word meanings and examples with your group.

| ① Don't Know | ② Recognize | ③ Familiar | ④ Know |

Word to Know	Meaning	Examples
1 **prepare** *verb* ① ② ③ ④	to get _____; to help make someone or something	I will **prepare** for the test by _____ _____ _____ _____
2 **focus** *verb* ① ② ③ ④	to give special _____ to something or someone	_____ _____ can make it difficult for teens to **focus** in class.
3 **mentor** *noun* ① ② ③ ④	someone who _____ another person with less knowledge or experience	A **mentor** could be very helpful for someone new at _____ _____ _____
4 **field** *noun* ① ② ③ ④	a person's area of _____; a subject of study	_____ _____ can be useful if you want to work in an international **field**.
1 **expertise** *noun* ① ② ③ ④	special _____ or _____ in a particular subject	My father relies on my help because of my **expertise** with _____ _____ _____
2 **professional** *noun* ① ② ③ ④	someone who _____ in a job that requires special education or training	Becoming a medical **professional** requires _____ _____ _____
3 **resilience** *noun* ① ② ③ ④	the ability to return to _____ after a difficult _____	The people affected by the hurricane showed great **resilience** by _____ _____ _____
4 **specialty** *noun* ① ② ③ ④	a person's particular _____ or area of study	Olympic athletes have many **specialties**, such as _____ _____

Academic Discussion
HOW SHOULD SCHOOL PREPARE STUDENTS FOR THE FUTURE?

 BRAINSTORM IDEAS

Briefly record at least two ideas in each column using everyday English.

Experiences	Academics
• bring in professionals to teach/lecture • •	• offer technical classes • •

 ANALYZE WORDS

Complete the chart with precise words to discuss and write about the topic.

Everyday	Precise
set up *(verb)*	arrange,
job *(noun)*	occupation,
bring in *(verb)*	enlist,

 MAKE A CLAIM

Rewrite two ideas using the frames and precise words. Then prepare to elaborate verbally.

> **Language to ELABORATE**
>
> To demonstrate, _____.
>
> In my experience, _____.

1. **Frame:** In my opinion, schools should prepare students for the future by _____ (**verb** + *–ing*: teaching, offering, providing)

   Response: _____

   _____

2. **Frame:** From my perspective, schools should teach students _____ (**adjective:** technical, academic, professional) skills that develop _____ (**noun:** expertise, knowledge, experience)

   Response: _____

   _____

 COLLABORATE

Listen attentively, restate, and record your partner's ideas.

> **Language to RESTATE**
>
> So if I understand you correctly, your perspective is that _____.
>
> Yes, that's accurate.
>
> Actually, what I (related/ specified) is that _____.

Classmate's Name	Ideas
	1.
	2.

Ten-Minute Paper

A **ten-minute paper** begins with a **claim,** followed by **two detail sentences** that elaborate with relevant examples and precise words.

Language to COMPARE IDEAS

My perspective on _____ is (similar to/different from) _____'s.

 PRESENT IDEAS

Listen, compare ideas, and take notes. Then indicate if you agree (+) or disagree (–).

Classmate's Name	Idea	+/–

ELABORATE IN WRITING

Work with a partner to write a ten-minute paper.

Language to COLLABORATE

What should we write?

We could select _____. What do you think seems reasonable?

Additionally, we could write _____.

In my opinion, schools should prepare students for the future by engaging professionals to share their work experiences. For example, a professional in the field of _____ could visit a school and _____ _____ about the _____ and _____ students need to succeed in that field. As a result, teens can take _____ that will _____ those skills, and become better prepared for _____

Write a ten-minute paper.

From my perspective, schools should teach students _____ skills that develop _____

For example, students interested in _____ could spend several hours a week at _____ where they would help _____

As a result, they will understand _____ and the experience they gain will make them more _____ to _____

Words to Go

 BUILD WORD KNOWLEDGE

Complete the meaning and examples for this high-utility academic word.

Word to Go	Meaning	Examples
principle prin·ci·ple *noun*	a basic rule or _____	Our family meetings work on the **principle** that each person _____ _____ _____ The **principle** of _____ _____ is important in my friendships.

DISCUSS & WRITE EXAMPLES

Discuss your response with a partner. Then complete the sentence in writing.

Peer assessment is based on the **principle** that personal _____

_____ play no part in judgments.

Write your response and read it aloud to a partner.

When school officials announced locker searches, we staged a protest about the

_____ of _____

 BUILD WORD KNOWLEDGE

Complete the meaning and examples for this high-utility academic word.

Word to Go	Meaning	Examples
adapt a·dapt *verb*	to _____ so that you can _____ in a different situation	After moving last year, I found it hard to **adapt** to _____ _____ _____ My _____ has been waking me up earlier, but I've **adapted** to the new schedule.

DISCUSS & WRITE EXAMPLES

Discuss your response with a partner. Then complete the sentence in writing.

Some students complained when the cafeteria stopped _____

_____ but most of us **adapted** to the new diet.

Write your response and read it aloud to a partner.

The boys on the baseball team are _____ to having girls

_____

Close Reading

BUILD FLUENCY

Read the text "Look to the Future" (*Issues,* pp. 89–93).

IDENTIFY KEY IDEAS & DETAILS

Take turns asking and answering questions with a partner. Then write brief notes.

Discussion Frames	Text Notes
Q: What is the text **primarily about?** **A:** The text is **primarily about** _____.	• how teens can _____ for their future _____
Q: What are the **most essential details** in this text? **A:** (One/An additional) **essential detail** in this article is _____.	• teens should begin _____ careers as early as _____ • spending time with _____ and _____ can help students figure out what they want to do • prospective employers look for _____ so teens should look for _____ _____

RESPOND WITH EVIDENCE

Use the frames and evidence from the text to construct a formal written response.

1. According to the author, what do career counselors consider when helping teens?

   According to the author, career counselors look at teens' favorite _____ _____ when helping them decide on a career.

   Counselors also consider students' _____

Use the frame to analyze the author's development of ideas.

2. What is the purpose of the vacation analogy in paragraph 10?

   The purpose of the analogy is to compare _____

   to _____ When packing for a vacation, you need to know _____ When preparing for a career,

   you need to know _____

IDENTIFY PRECISE WORDS

Review Text 1 and your *Portfolio* (pp. 182–187) to identify words for your writing.

Topic Words	High-Utility Academic Words
• career	• groundwork
•	•
•	•

Academic Discussion

HOW CAN ADOLESCENTS DEVELOP SKILLS FOR THE WORKPLACE?

 BRAINSTORM IDEAS

Briefly record at least two ideas in each column using everyday English.

Knowledge	Communication Skills
• internships	• practice public speaking
•	•
•	•

 ANALYZE WORDS

Complete the chart with precise words to discuss and write about the issue.

Everyday	Precise
figure out *(verb)*	determine,
needed *(adjective)*	obligatory,
watch *(verb)*	observe,

MAKE A CLAIM

Rewrite two ideas using the frames and precise words. Then prepare to elaborate verbally.

Language to ELABORATE

To demonstrate, _____.

In my experience, _____.

1. **Frame:** One way that adolescents can develop skills for the workplace is by _____ (**verb + –ing:** acquiring, identifying, taking)

   Response: _____

   _____

2. **Frame:** To develop skills for the workplace, adolescents can _____ (**base verb:** focus, locate, participate)

   Response: _____

   _____

 COLLABORATE

Listen attentively, restate, and record your partner's ideas.

Language to RESTATE

So, if I understand you correctly, your perspective is that _____.

Yes, that's accurate.

Actually, what I (related/specified) is that _____.

Classmate's Name	Ideas
	1.
	2.

Ten-Minute Paper

A **ten-minute paper** begins with a **claim,** followed by **two detail sentences** that elaborate with relevant examples and precise words.

 PRESENT IDEAS

Listen, compare ideas, and take notes. Then indicate if you agree (+) or disagree (–).

Classmate's Name	Idea	+/–

ELABORATE IN WRITING
Work with a partner to write a ten-minute paper.

One way that adolescents can develop skills for the workplace is by applying for internships. For example, teens who are interested in _____ _____ can look for internships at _____ or _____ As a result, interns will learn about _____ and will gain _____ that future employers may require.

Write a ten-minute paper.

To develop skills for the workplace, adolescents can _____ _____ For example, a teen who has ambitions of working in the field of _____ might _____ As a result, the adolescent will _____ what it takes to _____ and can begin to _____

Words to Go

BUILD WORD KNOWLEDGE

Complete the meanings and examples for these high-utility academic words.

Words to Go	Meanings	Examples
persist per·sist *verb*	to _____ doing something difficult	If you **persist** in _____ _____ _____ you will probably do better on the math test.
persistence per·sis·tence *noun*	the determination to _____ doing something difficult	My parents let me _____ _____ _____ because my **persistence** wore them down.

DISCUSS & WRITE EXAMPLES

Discuss your response with a partner. Then complete the sentence in writing.

The cyberbully **persisted** in _____

_____ until the school investigated the threats.

Write your response and read it aloud to a partner.

The students' _____ paid off when the principal agreed to let

students _____

BUILD WORD KNOWLEDGE

Complete the meaning and examples for this high-utility academic word.

Word to Go	Meaning	Examples
technical tech·ni·cal *adjective*	of or having to do with _____ engineering, mechanics, or _____ things work	I called customer service because I needed **technical** support for my _____ Technical training helped my brother become (a/an) _____

DISCUSS & WRITE EXAMPLES

Discuss your response with a partner. Then complete the sentence in writing.

The _____

in math class was having **technical** problems, so we had to use paper and pens.

Write your response and read it aloud to a partner.

Someone with little _____ knowledge will probably not be able to

help you with your _____

Section Shrink

 BUILD FLUENCY

Read Section 1 of "Learning That Works" (*Issues,* pp. 94–95).

 IDENTIFY KEY IDEAS & DETAILS

Take turns asking and answering questions with a partner. Then write brief notes.

Discussion Frames	Text Notes
Q: What does this section **focus on**? **A:** This section **focuses on** _____.	• hands-on _____ science classes that prepare students for _____
Q: What are the **significant details** in this section? **A:** (One/An additional) **significant detail** in this section is _____. **A:** Perhaps the **most significant detail** in this section is _____.	• McBride wanted to teach _____ skills; at first, superintendent thought _____ were more important • now superintendent thinks it's a great way to teach _____ • almost all students in the program _____ state tests; less than _____ of kids in _____ classes passed

 SUMMARIZE

"Shrink" Section 1 of the text by writing a summary in 40 or fewer words.

CLASS SUMMARY   **WORD COUNT:** _____

In Clyde McBride's program, classes that _____ in teaching
_____ and _____ skills
_____ students for careers in those fields and provide
_____ in fundamental subjects.

PARTNER SUMMARY   **WORD COUNT:** _____

Clyde McBride's agricultural sciences program _____
the _____ students will need for careers
in _____
while also teaching the _____ for academic success.

IDENTIFY PRECISE WORDS

Review Section 1 and your *Portfolio* (pp. 188–191) to identify words for your writing.

Topic Words	High-Utility Academic Words
• technicians	• hands-on
•	•
•	•

Words to Go

 BUILD WORD KNOWLEDGE

Complete the meanings and examples for these high-utility academic words.

Words to Go	Meanings	Examples
establish es·tab·lish *verb*	to _____ something that will last for some time	Teens who establish _____ _____ _____ habits are more likely to become healthy adults.
establishment es·tab·lish·ment *noun*	the people who are in _____ of a society or _____	Graffiti is often seen as _____ by the art establishment.

 DISCUSS & WRITE EXAMPLES

Discuss your response with a partner. Then complete the sentence in writing.

When our school **established** _____

last year, I signed up right away.

Write your response and read it aloud to a partner.

Many people claim that the beauty _____ promotes

_____

 BUILD WORD KNOWLEDGE

Complete the meaning and examples for this high-utility academic word.

Word to Go	Meaning	Examples
notion no·tion *noun*	an _____ or belief	My grandfather's **notion** of technology is _____ _____ . Parents and teens seem to have different **notions** about the purpose of _____

 DISCUSS & WRITE EXAMPLES

Discuss your response with a partner. Then complete the sentence in writing.

The **notion** of putting most of my allowance into savings seems _____

_____

Write your response and read it aloud to a partner.

Many people once had mistaken _____ about _____

_____ but now people know better.

Section Shrink

 BUILD FLUENCY

Read Section 2 of "Learning That Works" (*Issues*, pp. 95–98).

 IDENTIFY KEY IDEAS & DETAILS

Take turns asking and answering questions with a partner. Then write brief notes.

Discussion Frames	Text Notes
Q: What does this section **focus on**? **A:** This section **focuses on** _____.	• the benefits of _____ _____
Q: What are the **significant details** in this section? **A:** (One/An additional) **significant detail** in this section is _____. **A:** Perhaps the **most significant detail** in this section is _____.	• high _____ for high school graduates not in school • _____ provides skills that focus on teens' _____ and lead to _____ • 98.5% of East Valley Institute of Technology students _____ • Arizona's state superintendent praises _____ learning

 SUMMARIZE

"Shrink" Section 2 of the text by writing a summary in 40 or fewer words.

CLASS SUMMARY   **WORD COUNT:** _____

The _____ education students receive on the _____

_____ can improve _____

_____ and provide better preparation for _____

PARTNER SUMMARY   **WORD COUNT:** _____

_____ education gives students _____

_____ in fields that _____

which results in _____ and graduates who are

_____ for work.

IDENTIFY PRECISE WORDS

Review Section 2 and your *Portfolio* (pp. 192–193) to identify words for your writing.

Topic Words	High-Utility Academic Words
• certified skills	• suited
•	•
•	•

Words to Go

BUILD WORD KNOWLEDGE

Complete the meanings and examples for these high-utility academic words.

Words to Go	Meanings	Examples
reluctant re·luc·tant *adjective*	not _____ to do something	I was **reluctant** to let my brother _____ _____ _____
reluctantly re·luc·tant·ly *adverb*	in a _____ or _____ way	After I promised to _____ _____ my mother **reluctantly** gave me permission to attend the party.

DISCUSS & WRITE EXAMPLES

Discuss your response with a partner. Then complete the sentence in writing.

Some students are **reluctant** to _____

_____ even though it is a school rule.

Write your response and read it aloud to a partner.

I wanted to go to the movies with my friends, but I _____ agreed

to _____

BUILD WORD KNOWLEDGE

Complete the meaning and examples for this high-utility academic word.

Word to Go	Meaning	Examples
bias bi·as *noun*	an _____ about whether a person, group, or idea is _____ or _____	My cousin has a **bias** against my new friend just because she _____ _____ _____ My MP3 player shows my **bias** for _____

DISCUSS & WRITE EXAMPLES

Discuss your response with a partner. Then complete the sentence in writing.

Statistics on car accidents prove that **biases** against _____

are valid.

Write your response and read it aloud to a partner.

The debate about changes in the athletic department showed that school officials have

several _____ against allowing _____

_____

Section Shrink

BUILD FLUENCY

Read Section 3 of "Learning That Works" (*Issues*, pp. 98–101).

IDENTIFY KEY IDEAS & DETAILS

Take turns asking and answering questions with a partner. Then write brief notes.

Discussion Frames	Text Notes
Q: What does this section **focus on**? **A:** This section **focuses on** _____.	• _____ to voc-ed and its _____
Q: What are the **significant details** in this section? **A:** (One/An additional) **significant detail** in this section is _____. **A:** Perhaps the **most significant detail** in this section is _____.	• hard to _____ vocational schools; Democrats push for _____ and Republicans _____ to spend money • home high schools often _____ voc-ed participation • many say schools have a responsibility to create good _____; voc-ed proponents say it teaches _____ and how to be _____

SUMMARIZE

"Shrink" Section 3 of the text by writing a summary in 40 or fewer words.

CLASS SUMMARY   **WORD COUNT:** _____

_____ may prepare students for _____

cost less, and create _____ but vocational education

gives students the _____ and _____ skills

to be exceptional employees who _____ to their communities.

PARTNER SUMMARY   **WORD COUNT:** _____

Opponents of _____ cite

the _____ and need to develop good _____

but supporters say they involve _____

and emphasize _____

IDENTIFY PRECISE WORDS

Review Section 3 and your *Portfolio* (pp. 194–195) to identify words for your writing.

Topic Words	High-Utility Academic Words
• tech-track	• ideological
•	•
•	•

Student Writing Model

Academic Writing Type

A **formal written summary** provides an objective overview of the topic and important details from an informational text. The writer credits the author, but writes in primarily his or her own words, without including personal opinions.

    A. The **topic sentence** includes the text type, title, author, and topic.

    B. Detail sentences include the important details from the summarized text.

    C. The **concluding sentence** restates the author's conclusion in the writer's own words.

ANALYZE TEXT

Read this student model to analyze the elements of a formal summary.

A

    In the magazine article titled "Look to the Future," Betsy O'Donovan discusses how teens can prepare for careers. O'Donovan begins by reporting that the government expects the number of jobs in the United States to increase by 2016.

B

The writer continues to point out that teens should establish their career paths early on so they can focus on the courses they need and find mentors. She explains further that career interest tests can help teens identify fields they may want to pursue. Moreover, the writer notes that teens should shadow professionals so that they can experience particular jobs.

C

O'Donovan concludes by emphasizing that employers want workers who are resilient and can adapt to unfamiliar situations.

MARK & DISCUSS ELEMENTS

Mark the summary elements and use the frames to discuss them with your partner.

1. **Number (1–4) the four elements of the topic sentence.** *The topic sentence includes the _____.*

2. **Draw a box around four transition words or phrases.** *One transition (word/phrase) is _____.*

3. **Underline four important details.** *One important detail in this summary is _____.*

4. **Circle four citation verbs.** *One citation verb that the writer uses is _____.*

5. **Star four precise topic words and check four high-utility academic words.** *An example of a (precise topic word/high-utility academic word) is _____.*

Organize a Formal Summary

Prompt | Write a formal summary of "Learning That Works."

Guidelines for Paraphrasing Multiple Sentences
Paraphrase related details from a source text by combining key information into one sentence. Replace key words and phrases with synonyms and keep important topic words.

Text Detail 1	Text Detail 2	Text Detail 3
"High school dropout rates continue to be a national embarrassment" (Klein 96).	"The unemployment rate for recent high school graduates who are not in school is a stratospheric 33 percent" (Klein 96).	"'But according to the Bureau of Labor Statistics, less than a quarter of new job openings will require a bachelor of arts degree.'" (Klein 96).

 PARAPHRASE IDEAS

Combine key information from the text details above into one detail sentence.

Klein argues that college prep for all students has resulted in

(Text Detail 1) _____

(Text Detail 2) _____ and

(Text Detail 3) _____

PLAN KEY IDEAS & DETAILS

State the text information to write a topic sentence.

In the magazine article titled (title) _____

(author's full name) _____ (citation verb: presents, examines, investigates)

_____ (topic) _____

List four important details from the text using primarily your own words.

1. _____
_____

2. _____
_____

3. _____
_____

4. _____
_____

Restate the conclusion in your own words.

_____
_____

Write a Formal Summary

Prompt | Write a formal summary of "Learning That Works."

✎ **WRITE A PARAGRAPH**

Use the frame to write your topic sentence, detail sentences, and concluding sentence.

A

In the _____ titled _____
    (text type)   (title)

_____   _____   _____
(author's full name)   (citation verb)   (topic)

_____

B

_____ begins by _____
(Author's last name)   (citation verb + –ing: presenting, arguing)

_____ (1st important detail)

_____

_____

The (author/writer/researcher) _____ continues to

_____   _____
(citation verb, base form: describe, report)   (2nd important detail)

_____

_____

(He/She) _____ _____ further that
                                   (present-tense citation verb)

_____ (3rd important detail)

_____

_____

Moreover, the (author/writer/researcher) _____

_____   _____
(present-tense citation verb)   (4th important detail)

_____

_____

_____

C

_____ concludes by _____ that
(Author's last name)   (citation verb + –ing: suggesting, emphasizing)

_____ (restate conclusion)

_____

_____

_____

Rate Your Formal Summary

Scoring Guide	
1	Insufficient
2	Developing
3	Sufficient
4	Exemplary

ASSESS YOUR DRAFT

Rate your formal summary. Then have a partner rate it.

1. Does the topic sentence state the text type, title, author, and topic?	Self	1	2	3	4
	Partner	1	2	3	4
2. Did you paraphrase the most important details from the text?	Self	1	2	3	4
	Partner	1	2	3	4
3. Did you use citation verbs to credit the author?	Self	1	2	3	4
	Partner	1	2	3	4
4. Did you include precise topic words and high-utility academic words?	Self	1	2	3	4
	Partner	1	2	3	4
5. Did you use transitions to introduce and sequence details?	Self	1	2	3	4
	Partner	1	2	3	4
6. Did you accurately restate the author's conclusion?	Self	1	2	3	4
	Partner	1	2	3	4

REFLECT & REVISE

Record specific priorities and suggestions to help you and your partner revise.

(Partner) Positive Feedback: I appreciate how you (used/included) _____

_____

_____

(Partner) Suggestion: As you revise your summary, focus on _____

_____

_____

(Self) Priority 1: My summary paragraph needs _____

_____

_____

(Self) Priority 2: I plan to improve my summary by _____

_____

_____

CHECK & EDIT

Use this checklist to proofread and edit your formal summary.

- ☐ Did you capitalize the title of the magazine article and proper nouns?
- ☐ Did you put quotation marks around the title of the magazine article?
- ☐ Did you use commas appropriately after transitions?
- ☐ Do simple present-tense verbs end in –*s*?
- ☐ Is each sentence complete?
- ☐ Are all words spelled correctly?

Academic Discussion
WHAT ARE THE ARGUMENTS SUPPORTING AND OPPOSING CAREER AND TECHNICAL EDUCATION?

 BRAINSTORM IDEAS

Briefly record at least two ideas in each column using everyday English.

Supporting Arguments	Opposing Arguments
• gives hands-on experience	• loses focus on academics
•	•
•	•

 ANALYZE WORDS

Complete the chart with precise words to discuss and write about the topic.

Everyday	Precise
pay no attention to *(verb phrase)*	disregard,
help *(verb)*	encourage,
mess with *(verb)*	disrupt,

 MAKE A CLAIM

Rewrite two ideas using the frames and precise words. Then prepare to elaborate verbally.

Language to ELABORATE

To demonstrate, _____.

In my experience, _____.

1. **Frame:** (Proponents/Opponents) argue that career and technical education _____ (**present-tense verb:** develops, prepares, wastes, segregates)

   Response: _____

   _____

2. **Frame:** One (supporting/opposing) argument is that career and technical education (benefits/harms) students by _____ (**verb + –ing:** training, building, preventing, denying)

   Response: _____

   _____

 COLLABORATE

Listen attentively, restate, and record your partner's ideas.

Language to RESTATE

So if I understand you correctly, your perspective is that _____.

Yes, that's accurate.

Actually, what I (related/ specified) is that _____.

Classmate's Name	Ideas
	1.
	2.

Ten-Minute Paper

A **ten-minute paper** begins with a **claim,** followed by **two detail sentences** that elaborate with relevant examples and precise words.

Language to COMPARE IDEAS

My perspective on _____ is (similar to/different from) _____'s.

 PRESENT IDEAS

Listen, compare ideas, and take notes. Then indicate if you agree (+) or disagree (−).

Classmate's Name	Idea	+/−

ELABORATE IN WRITING

Work with a partner to write a ten-minute paper.

Language to COLLABORATE

What should we write?

We could select _____. What do you think seems reasonable?

Additionally, we could write _____.

Proponents argue that career and technical education contributes to higher graduation rates. For example, at East Valley Institute of Technology in Arizona, students are _____

_____

As a result, _____

of the students _____

Write a ten-minute paper.

One _____ argument is that career and technical education

_____ students by _____

_____

For example, _____

_____

_____

As a result, _____

_____

Words to Go

BUILD WORD KNOWLEDGE

Complete the meanings and examples for these high-utility academic words.

Words to Go	Meanings	Examples
innovate in·no·vate *verb*	to introduce _____ ideas or methods of doing something	If our soccer team wants to win more games, we need to **innovate** and _____ _____
innovation in·no·va·tion *noun*	the introduction of _____ ideas or methods	A new _____ _____ won an award for **innovation** in technology.

DISCUSS & WRITE EXAMPLES

Discuss your response with a partner. Then complete the sentence in writing.

Before Henry Ford **innovated** the assembly line system for building automobiles, cars

were _____

Write your response and read it aloud to a partner.

Older generations can be reluctant to accept _____ such as

_____ and _____

BUILD WORD KNOWLEDGE

Complete the meaning and examples for this high-utility academic word.

Word to Go	Meaning	Examples
passive pas·sive *adjective*	tending to _____ conditions; not taking _____	_____ is an example of a **passive** character. My **passive** dog just sits there when _____ _____

DISCUSS & WRITE EXAMPLES

Discuss your response with a partner. Then complete the sentence in writing.

Environmental activists are not **passive** about _____

_____

Write your response and read it aloud to a partner.

Rather than being _____, victims of bullying should _____

_____

Close Reading

 BUILD FLUENCY
Read the text "Educating the Next Steve Jobs" (*Issues,* pp. 102–105).

 IDENTIFY KEY IDEAS & DETAILS
Take turns asking and answering questions with a partner. Then write brief notes.

Discussion Frames	Text Notes
Q: What is the text **primarily about**? A: The text is **primarily about** _____.	• preparing students to _____ _____
Q: What are the **most essential details** in this text? A: (One/An additional) **essential detail** in this text is _____.	• students learn to be _____ through _____ • innovative schools are _____ not _____ like conventional schools • being _____ is more important than _____

 RESPOND WITH EVIDENCE
Use the frame and evidence from the text to construct a formal written response.

1. According to the author, which practices do innovative schools reject?

   According to the author, practices that innovative schools reject are _____

   _____

   _____

   Moreover, innovative schools teach students to _____

   _____

Use the frame to analyze how the author develops ideas.

2. What is the author's claim? How does the author support his claim in paragraphs 3–6?

   The author's claim is that _____

   _____

   The author supports his claim by _____

   _____

   _____ to show how innovative schools succeed.

IDENTIFY PRECISE WORDS
Review Text 3 and your *Portfolio* (pp. 200–203) to identify words for your writing.

Topic Words	High-Utility Academic Words
• conventional	• persevere
•	•
•	•

Take a Stand

Debate Does school prepare students for their future careers?

COLLABORATE

Read the debate question about preparation for work. Then take turns using a frame to respond with your initial reaction.

Language to RESPOND

So, _____, what's your initial reaction?

My initial reaction is _____.

_____ and I had (similar/somewhat different) initial reactions.

ANALYZE SOURCES

Read a quote that either supports or opposes the debate topic. Then paraphrase.

Quote	Paraphrase
Model: "58% [of high school graduates] said their schools did a good job of preparing them for work, but 41% said they should have done better" (Hart Research Associates 88).	To paraphrase, a small _____ of high school graduates _____ their schools taught them _____
1. "School counselors often have access to career interest tests that they like to use with students too. Students can review the results with their school counselors, who can help them figure out the next steps" (O'Donovan 91).	The author seems to be saying that schools have _____ to help students identify _____ _____ and assist them in _____ their chosen fields.
2. "The unemployment rate for recent high school graduates who are not in school is a stratospheric 33 percent" (Klein 96).	To paraphrase, _____ of high school graduates who are not pursuing further _____ are _____
3. "'It's easier to learn engineering by actually building a house—which my family did when I was a kid, by the way—than sitting in a classroom figuring out the process in the abstract'" (Klein 98).	To paraphrase, students who receive _____ learn _____ skills such as _____ more thoroughly.
4. ". . . the most important thing educators can do to prepare students for work in companies like [Google] is to teach them that problems can never be understood or solved in the context of a single academic discipline" (Wagner 103).	The author seems to be saying that _____ want students who have learned to _____ by working on _____ at the same time.

Debate Ideas

SYNTHESIZE IDEAS

Write a response to the debate question, including a paraphrase of a text quote and elaboration on the quote.

Claim: My position is that school (does/does not) _____ prepare students

for their future careers.

Transitional Statement: I have (one key reason/a compelling reason) _____

_____ for taking this stance.

Quote Paraphrase: (According to _____,/The author points out _____.)

_____

_____

_____

Quote Elaboration: (As a result, _____./Consequently, _____.)

_____

_____

_____

PRESENT EVIDENCE

Including Visual Displays

When presenting ideas during class or in a meeting, include a **visual display**. Consider including images or graphics to express information, strengthen claims and evidence, and add interest.

LISTEN & TAKE NOTES

Listen attentively and take notes. Then indicate if you agree (+) or disagree (–).

> **Language to AFFIRM & CLARIFY**
>
> That's a compelling stance.
> What exactly do you mean by _____?

Classmate's Name	Idea	+/–

Student Writing Model

Academic Writing Type

An **argument** states a claim and supports it with logical reasons and relevant evidence from sources.

A. The **thesis statement** clearly states the writer's claim and tells what the writer will explain about the topic.

B. **Supporting paragraphs** support the claim with reasons and evidence from sources. The writer also presents counterclaims and responds with strong evidence.

C. The **conclusion statement** restates the writer's claim about the issue.

ANALYZE TEXT
Read this student model to analyze elements of an argument.

A

After examining the issues surrounding schools and job skills, I am convinced that school does prepare students for their future careers.

B

One reason I maintain this position is that most students have access to valuable career guidance in their own schools. In "Look to the Future," Betsy O'Donovan presents compelling data regarding the positive consequences of providing job skills to students. For example, counselors can give students interest tests and advise them on a course of study (91). Opponents of relying on conventional schools to prepare students for their professional lives tend to highlight the need for innovative programs that provide technical training. However, current data from Hart Research Associates actually demonstrate that more than half of high school graduates believe their schools prepared them well for work (88).

I am also in favor of current career training due to the advantages of offering students choices. Joe Klein emphasizes in "Learning That Works" that vocational education can improve test scores and graduation rates. One particularly convincing statistic is that 27 percent of students in Arizona participate in career and technical education (97).

C

Whether school teaches the skills required for work after graduation will remain a controversial issue. After reviewing relevant data, I maintain that students are learning what they need to know for their future careers.

MARK & DISCUSS ELEMENTS

Mark the argument elements and use the frames to discuss them with your partner.

1. **Circle the writer's claim within the thesis statement.** *The writer's claim is _____.*

2. **Underline and label two reasons that support the writer's claim with the letter *R*.**

   One reason that supports the writer's claim is _____.

3. **Underline and label four pieces of evidence that support the writer's claim with the letter *E*.** *One piece of evidence that supports the writer's claim is _____.*

4. **Draw a box around a counterclaim.** *One counterclaim is _____.*

5. **Star four precise topic words and check four high-utility academic words.**

   An example of a (precise topic word/high-utility academic word) is _____.

ASSESS A STUDENT SAMPLE

Read an additional student sample and rate it.

Scoring Guide			
1	Insufficient	3	Sufficient
2	Developing	4	Exemplary

1. Does the thesis statement clearly state the claim?	1	2	3	4
2. Do supporting paragraphs begin with a topic sentence that specifies a reason?	1	2	3	4
3. Did the writer give evidence drawn primarily from sources to support the claim?	1	2	3	4
4. Did the writer explain why the evidence is relevant and significant?	1	2	3	4
5. Did the writer include complex sentences to present and respond to counterclaims?	1	2	3	4
6. Did the writer use strong verbs and verb phrases to express opinions?	1	2	3	4
7. Did the writer use transitions to introduce reasons and evidence?	1	2	3	4
8. Did the writer use precise adjectives to describe evidence?	1	2	3	4
9. Did the writer include citation information for text evidence?	1	2	3	4
10. Did the writer include precise topic words and high-utility words?	1	2	3	4
11. Does the conclusion statement strongly restate the claim using new wording?	1	2	3	4

REFLECT & REVISE

Record specific priorities and suggestions to help the writer.

I appreciated the student's (effort to/use of/skillful) _____

_____

_____

_____

One suggestion I have to revise this argument research paper is to _____

_____

_____

_____

Another suggestion I have to strengthen this argument research paper is to _____

_____

_____

Precise Adjectives

Guidelines for Using Precise Adjectives to Describe Evidence

Precise adjectives describe nouns vividly and make your writing more interesting. Use precise adjectives to describe the data, statistics, and other evidence you present to support your claim.

Everyday Adjectives	Precise Adjectives
good	convincing, strong, compelling, relevant, striking
scary	alarming, distressing, unnerving, striking, disturbing
interesting	fascinating, intriguing, thought-provoking, provocative, controversial
hard	difficult, troubling, challenging, complex, complicated, perplexing
new	recent, current, up-to-date
enough/true-sounding	sufficient, adequate, substantial, believable, convincing
silly	absurd, preposterous, ridiculous, unreasonable
untrue	unfounded, groundless, baseless, unsubstantiated

 WRITE PRECISE ADJECTIVES

Complete the sentences with precise adjectives.

1. (A/An) _____ argument against mandating online courses is the lack of research proving they are as effective as conventional classes.

2. _____ evidence proves that the number of young people claiming bankruptcy is increasing.

3. Although a common argument against later school start times is that bus schedules would need to change, I don't find the evidence _____

Use precise adjectives to complete the sentences about the claim.

Claim: States should mandate online courses for students.

1. **Evidence:** In "Cyber Students," Adele Birkenes presents _____ data regarding the positive consequences of requiring online courses.

2. **Evidence:** One particularly _____ statistic is that more than 30 percent of college students take one or more online courses.

3. **Counterclaim:** Although a common argument against online education is that it may not be comparable to face-to-face education, I don't find the evidence

_____

4. **Response to Counterclaim:** Clearly, there is _____ evidence that proves online courses are not as effective as conventional classes.

5. **Restating Claim:** After reviewing _____ data, I contend that online courses should be mandatory.

Simple & Complex Sentences

Guidelines for Using Simple & Complex Sentences

Use **simple and complex sentences** to present and respond to counterclaims in your argument.

Presenting Counterclaims

A _____ (adjective: common, pervasive, consistent) argument (in favor of/against) _____ is _____.

(Opponents/Proponents) of _____ tend to _____. (verb: emphasize, point out, highlight)

Although a common argument (in favor of/against) _____ is _____, I don't find the evidence _____. (adjective: compelling, substantial, believable)

Examples

A consistent argument in favor of raising the driving age is that it will reduce fatal crashes.

Opponents of changing school start times **tend to emphasize** the inconvenience of adjusting bus schedules.

Although a common argument in favor of mandating online courses is that they prepare students for college, **I don't find the evidence compelling.**

Responding to Counterclaims

(Current data/Recent findings/Studies) actually demonstrate that _____.

Clearly, there is (sufficient/adequate/striking) evidence that (shows/proves) _____.

Examples

Studies actually demonstrate that bilingual people are cognitively flexible.

Clearly, there is sufficient evidence that proves credit cards can be dangerous for teenagers.

✎ WRITE COUNTERCLAIMS

Work with the teacher to write a counterclaim and response.

Claim: Schools should not change start times.

Counterclaim: (A/An) adjective: common, pervasive, consistent) _____ argument in favor of starting school later is that it improves attendance.

Response: Clearly, there is (sufficient/adequate/striking) _____ evidence that _____

Work with a partner to write a counterclaim and response.

Claim: Schools should require world-language study.

Counterclaim: Although a common argument _____ is

_____ I don't find the evidence _____

Response: _____ actually demonstrate that _____ .

_____

Work on your own to write a counterclaim and response.

Claim: Our state should not change the driving age.

Counterclaim: _____

_____

Response: _____

_____

Organize an Argument

Prompt Does school prepare students for their future careers? Write an argument that states your claim and supports it with text evidence.

Guidelines for Using Direct Quotes to Cite Text Evidence

Use a direct quote from an authority on a topic to reinforce your argument or to accentuate an idea. Avoid quotes that are longer than three lines, and enclose the exact words of the source in quotation marks (" "). Include a citation that indicates the source of the quote.

Incorporating Quotes	Examples
Introduce the quote with a complete sentence and a colon.	Joe Klein argues that vocational education can still breed good citizens: "But people with jobs, especially skilled jobs, tend to be better citizens than those without them" (100).
Use an introductory phrase.	According to Tony Wagner, "at the most innovative schools, classes are 'hands-on,' and students are creators, not mere consumers" (103).
Blend the quote into your own sentence.	The advice that students "research, job shadow, and ask for informational interviews" strongly suggests that schools may not provide students the career experiences they need (O'Donovan 91).

WRITE A THESIS STATEMENT

Describe your claim.

My claim: _____

_____

Use academic language to restate your claim as a thesis statement.

_____ high schools and jobs,
(Thesis starter)

I (agree/disagree) _____ (strongly/firmly) _____

that _____
(your claim)

 CHOOSE SUPPORTING TOPICS

List each topic you will write about to support your claim.

Supporting Paragraph 1

Topic: _____

Supporting Paragraph 2

Topic: _____

Find a quote from the texts that supports your claim and incorporate it into a sentence.

_____

_____

_____

_____

PLAN SUPPORTING PARAGRAPHS

List reasons and evidence that support your claim. You may draw from texts, your experience, or a classmate's experience.

Supporting Paragraph 1

Reason 1: _____

_____

Evidence: _____

_____

Source/Page Number: _____

Author: _____

Counterclaim: _____

_____

Response to Counterclaim: _____

_____

Source: _____

Author: _____

Supporting Paragraph 2

Reason 2: _____

_____

Evidence: _____

_____

Source/Page Number: _____

Author: _____

Statistical Evidence: _____

_____

Source: _____

✏ **WRITE A CONCLUSION**

Plan a conclusion that restates your claim.

Whether _____
        (restate the issue)

_____ will remain a controversial issue.

After reviewing _____ data, I _____
               (precise adjective)   (verb/verb phrase to express opinion)

that _____
     (restate your claim)

_____

_____

Write an Argument

Prompt | Does school prepare students for their future careers? Write an argument that states your claim and supports it with text evidence.

 WRITE A RESEARCH PAPER
Use the frame to write your thesis statement, supporting paragraphs, and conclusion statement.

A

_____
(Thesis starter)

_____
(topic)

I _____ that _____
 (verb/verb phrase to express opinion)   (your claim)

_____

B1

One reason I maintain this position is that _____
 (1st reason that supports your claim)

_____

_____

_____

In _____
 (title of source)

_____ presents _____ data
(author's full name)   (precise adjective)

regarding the (positive/negative) _____ consequences of

_____
(topic)

For example, _____
 (evidence from source)

_____

_____

(Opponents/Proponents) _____ of _____
                                                        (topic)

tend to (verb: emphasize, point out, highlight) _____

_____
(counterclaim)

However, (current data/studies) _____ actually demonstrate

that _____
 (your response to counterclaim)

_____

_____

B2

I am also (in favor of/opposed to) _____

_____
(topic)

due to _____
(2nd reason that supports your claim)

_____

_____

_____ emphasizes in _____
(Author's full name)   (title of source)

that _____
(evidence from a different source)

_____

_____

One particularly _____ statistic is _____
(precise adjective)   (statistic from a source)

_____

_____

_____

C

Whether _____
(restate the issue)

_____

_____ will remain a controversial issue.

After reviewing _____ data, I _____
(precise adjective)   (verb/verb phrase to express opinion)

that _____
(restate your claim)

_____

_____

_____

Two-Minute Speech

IDENTIFY TOPIC

Choose one of the questions below to address in a two-minute speech.

☐ Should our state require students to take at least one online course per year?

☐ Should our school provide internships for career education?

BRAINSTORM IDEAS

Write your claim and two reasons that support it.

My Claim: _____

Reason 1: _____

Reason 2: _____

SYNTHESIZE IDEAS

Take notes on supporting evidence and a counterclaim.

Evidence 1: _____

_____

Evidence 2: _____

_____

Counterclaim: _____

_____

Response: _____

_____

WRITE A SPEECH

Write a two-minute speech that states your claim and includes reasons, evidence, and a counterclaim.

From my point of view, _____

_____

One reason is that _____

_____

_____

Secondly, _____

_____

For example, _____

_____

_____

Critics might claim that _____

_____

However, _____

_____

For these reasons, I _____ that _____

_____

Present & Rate Your Speech

Including Visual Displays

When presenting ideas during class or in a meeting, include a **visual display.** Consider including images or graphics to express information, strengthen claims and evidence, and add interest.

 PRESENT YOUR SPEECH

Present your speech to the small group. Make sure to include a visual display and explain it.

 LISTEN & TAKE NOTES

Listen attentively and take notes. Then indicate if you agree (+) or disagree (–).

> **Language to AFFIRM & CLARIFY**
>
> That's a compelling stance.
>
> What exactly do you mean by _____?

Classmate's Name	Idea	+/-

 ASSESS YOUR SPEECH

Use the Scoring Guide to rate your speech.

Scoring Guide			
1	Insufficient	3	Sufficient
2	Developing	4	Exemplary

	1	2	3	4
1. Did your topic sentence clearly state your claim?	1	2	3	4
2. Did you include strong reasons and evidence to support your speech?	1	2	3	4
3. Did you include precise topic words?	1	2	3	4
4. Were you easy to understand?	1	2	3	4
5. Did you include a visual display?	1	2	3	4

REFLECT

Think of two ways you can improve for your next speech.

Priority 1: I can enhance my next speech by _____

_____

_____

Priority 2: In my next speech, I will incorporate _____

_____

_____

SHOULD EVERYONE HAVE TO TURN OUT TO VOTE?

 BUILD KNOWLEDGE
Read and respond to the Data File (*Issues,* p. 106).

 BRAINSTORM IDEAS
Write a brief list of the benefits of voting.

- voice your opinion
- _____
- _____
- _____

 PRESENT IDEAS
Use the frames to discuss ideas with your group. Listen attentively and record the strongest ideas to complete the concept web.

Language to FACILITATE DISCUSSION
So _____, what's your suggestion?
_____, what benefit did you come up with?

1. When you vote, you are able to _____ (**base verb:** voice)

2. Your vote can also _____ (**base verb:** affect)

3. A vote sends a message that you want to _____ (**base verb:** change)

4. Voting gives you the power to _____ (**base verb:** impact)

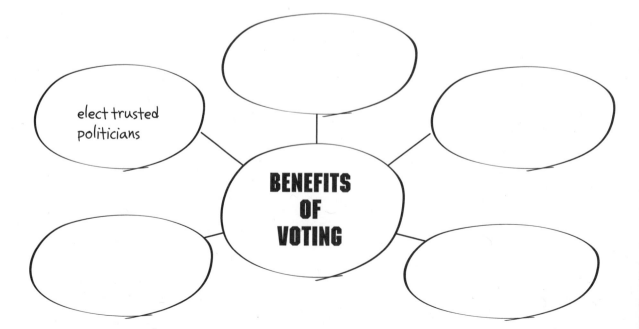

elect trusted politicians

BENEFITS OF VOTING

Words to Know

 BUILD WORD KNOWLEDGE

Rate your word knowledge. Then discuss word meanings and examples with your group.

	① Don't Know	② Recognize	③ Familiar	④ Know

Word to Know	Meaning	Examples
1 **duty** *noun* ① ② ③ ④	a thing a person _____ do because it is morally or _____ right	It is my **duty** as an older brother to _____ my younger brother.
2 **democratic** *adjective* ① ② ③ ④	referring to the idea that _____ should be involved in making _____	If _____ were more **democratic**, decisions would reflect the wishes of _____ instead of _____
3 **citizen** *noun* ① ② ③ ④	a person who has _____ as well as full _____ in a particular country or place	As a tax-paying **citizen**, my father feels that he shouldn't have to _____ _____
4 **civic** *adjective* ① ② ③ ④	of or having to do with a _____ or the _____ who live there	The _____ _____ in our town is a source of **civic** pride.
1 **obligation** *noun* ① ② ③ ④	something you _____ _____ because it is your responsibility or because you have promised	_____ _____ is an **obligation** that I take seriously.
2 **constitutional** *adjective* ① ② ③ ④	of or relating to the written document containing the basic _____ of the United States	I believe that _____ _____ are a violation of my **constitutional** right to privacy.
3 **representative** *adjective* ① ② ③ ④	describing a system of _____ made up of people who act and speak for the people who _____ for them	When Americans were under British rule, they had to _____ _____ even though they didn't have a **representative** government.
4 **contribution** *noun* ① ② ③ ④	something that a person _____ or _____ to help something succeed	I only _____ but I know that my **contribution** helped make the school play a success.

Academic Discussion
What are the reasons why some citizens do not vote?

BRAINSTORM IDEAS

Briefly record at least two ideas in each column using everyday English.

Personal Reasons	Political Reasons
• work long hours	• dislike the candidates
•	•
•	•

ANALYZE WORDS

Complete the chart with precise words to discuss and write about the topic.

Everyday	Precise
expect *(verb)*	anticipate,
boredom *(noun)*	indifference,
out of the way *(adjective)*	inaccessible,

MAKE A CLAIM

Rewrite two ideas using the frames and precise words. Then prepare to elaborate verbally.

Language to ELABORATE

To clarify, _____.

Based on my experience, _____.

1. **Frame:** From my point of view, one (personal/political) reason why some citizens do not vote is because they _____ (**present-tense verb:** have, forget, believe)

   Response: _____

   _____

2. **Frame:** I imagine that some citizens do not vote due to _____ (**noun phrase:** lack of time, other responsibilities, registration difficulties).

   Response: _____

   _____

COLLABORATE

Listen attentively, restate, and record your partner's ideas.

Language to RESTATE

In other words, your point of view is that _____.

Yes, that's accurate.

No. What I intended to say was _____.

Classmate's Name	Ideas
	1.
	2.

Ten-Minute Paper

A **ten-minute paper** begins with a **claim,** followed by **two detail sentences** that elaborate with relevant examples and precise words.

PRESENT IDEAS

Listen, compare ideas, and take notes. Then indicate if you agree (+) or disagree (–).

Classmate's Name	Idea	+/–

ELABORATE IN WRITING

Work with the teacher to write a ten-minute paper.

From my point of view, one personal reason why some citizens do not vote is because they forget to reregister to vote when they move. For example, when my family _____ last year, my parents forgot to _____ their _____ registration. As a result, when it was _____ they discovered that they were not _____ and they couldn't participate in that _____

Work with a partner to write a ten-minute paper.

I imagine that some citizens do not vote due to _____
_____

For example, _____
_____
_____

As a result, _____
_____

Words to Go

 BUILD WORD KNOWLEDGE

Complete the meaning and examples for this high-utility academic word.

Word to Go	Meaning	Examples
institution in·sti·tu·tion *noun*	a large _____ _____ that has a certain kind of work or purpose, especially of a public nature	Many financial **institutions** try to provide consumers with help in _____ _____ People who want to _____ _____ should think about a career in a political institution.

 DISCUSS & WRITE EXAMPLES

Discuss your response with a partner. Then complete the sentence in writing.

Environmental **institutions** educate the public about the dangers of certain actions such as _____

Write your response and read it aloud to a partner.

A health issue such as _____ is a major concern of the medical _____

BUILD WORD KNOWLEDGE

Complete the meaning and examples for this high-utility academic word.

Word to Go	Meaning	Examples
incentive in·cen·tive *noun*	something that _____ _____ you to do something	The chance to _____ _____ was an **incentive** for me to rake the leaves in the yard. Joining the _____ _____ had certain social incentives for me.

DISCUSS & WRITE EXAMPLES

Discuss your response with a partner. Then complete the sentence in writing.

I believe that driving privileges should not be used as an **incentive** to convince students to _____

Write your response and read it aloud to a partner.

The musical director told us that as an added _____ we would each receive a _____ if our glee club won the contest.

Close Reading

 BUILD FLUENCY

Read the text "Telling Americans to Vote, or Else" (*Issues,* pp. 107–111).

 IDENTIFY KEY IDEAS & DETAILS

Take turns asking and answering questions with a partner. Then write brief notes.

Discussion Frames	Text Notes
Q: What is a **central idea** in this text? A: A **central idea** in this text is _____.	• the United States should have _____ _____

Q: What are the **relevant supporting details** in this text?
 	
A: (One/An additional) **relevant supporting detail** in this text is _____.
	• voting _____ in 31 countries, like Australia, where turnout is about _____
	• pros: voters better _____;
	  more citizens _____;
	  less _____
	• many _____ mandated voting;
	  need to try & observe _____

 RESPOND WITH EVIDENCE

Use the frames and evidence from the text to construct a formal written response.

1. According to the author, what are two ways mandatory voting would affect politics?

   According to the author, mandatory voting would _____

   _____

   and _____

   _____

   Use the frame to analyze the author's purpose.

2. What is the effect of describing the success of mandatory voting in Australia? Why does the author include the information?

   One effect of describing the success of mandatory voting in Australia is to _____

   _____

   The author includes this information to _____

   _____

IDENTIFY PRECISE WORDS

Review Text 1 and your *Portfolio* (pp. 216–221) to identify words for your writing.

Topic Words	High-Utility Academic Words
• partisan	• prevalence
•	•
•	•

Academic Discussion
What are some ways in which people can engage in our democracy?

 BRAINSTORM IDEAS

Briefly record at least two ideas in each column using everyday English.

Individual	Collaborative
• learn about the issues	• join campaigns
•	•
•	•

 ANALYZE WORDS

Complete the chart with precise words to discuss and write about the issue.

Everyday	Precise
sign up *(verb phrase)*	enroll,
try to get votes *(verb phrase)*	canvass,
back *(verb)*	advocate for,

 MAKE A CLAIM

Rewrite two ideas using the frames and precise words. Then prepare to elaborate verbally.

Language to ELABORATE

To clarify, _____.

Based on my experience, _____.

1. **Frame:** One (individual/collaborative) way in which people can engage in our democracy is to _____ (**base verb:** vote, volunteer, serve, plan)

   Response: _____

   _____

2. **Frame:** (Individually/Collaboratively), people can make a contribution to our democracy by _____ (**verb + -ing:** joining, writing, discussing, organizing)

   Response: _____

COLLABORATE

Listen attentively, restate, and record your partner's ideas.

Language to RESTATE

In other words, your point of view is that _____.

Yes, that's accurate.

No. What I intended to say was _____.

Classmate's Name	Ideas
	1.
	2.

Ten-Minute Paper

A **ten-minute paper** begins with a **claim,** followed by **two detail sentences** that elaborate with relevant examples and precise words.

Language to COMPARE IDEAS

My point of view on _____ is (similar to/somewhat different from) _____'s.

 PRESENT IDEAS

Listen, compare ideas, and take notes. Then indicate if you agree (+) or disagree (–).

Classmate's Name	Idea	+/–

ELABORATE IN WRITING

Work with the teacher to write a ten-minute paper.

Language to COLLABORATE

What should we write?

We could select _____. What do you think is a strong selection?

As an alternative, we could write _____.

One collaborative way in which people can engage in our democracy is to canvass for the candidate they support. For example, people can go door-to-door _____ the residents of a particular _____ or _____ about the _____ and where he or she stands on the _____ As a result, some previously _____ _____ voters may decide to _____ the candidate.

Work with a partner to write a ten-minute paper.

_____ people can make a contribution to our democracy

by _____

_____

For example, _____

_____

_____

As a result, _____

_____

_____

Words to Go

 BUILD WORD KNOWLEDGE

Complete the meaning and examples for this high-utility academic word.

Word to Go	Meaning	Examples
dynamic dy·nam·ic *adjective*	constantly _____ _____ due to many influences	After seeing my mother work at a job that _____ I'm hoping for a career in a more **dynamic** field. Carla's varied _____ _____ make our friendship rather **dynamic**.

 DISCUSS & WRITE EXAMPLES

Discuss your response with a partner. Then complete the sentence in writing.

My personality becomes more **dynamic** when I _____

_____

Write your response and read it aloud to a partner.

Some people feel that traditional courses are not _____ enough to

keep up with _____

 BUILD WORD KNOWLEDGE

Complete the meaning and examples for this high-utility academic word.

Word to Go	Meaning	Examples
precede pre·cede *verb*	to come _____ something else	The principal's speech will **precede** our _____ _____ The movie was **preceded** by _____ _____

 DISCUSS & WRITE EXAMPLES

Discuss your response with a partner. Then complete the sentence in writing.

Many young people's overuse of _____

preceded their problems with excessive debt.

Write your response and read it aloud to a partner.

Because I stayed up late video chatting with friends the night _____

the exam, I _____

Section Shrink

 BUILD FLUENCY

Read Section 1 of the speech "What Does It Mean to Be an American Citizen?"
(*Issues*, pp. 112–113).

 IDENTIFY KEY IDEAS & DETAILS

Take turns asking and answering questions with a partner. Then write brief notes.

Discussion Frames	Text Notes
Q: What is a **central idea** in this section? **A:** A **central idea** in this section is _____.	• the debt of _____ owed by American _____
Q: What are the **relevant supporting details** in this section? **A:** (One/An additional) **relevant supporting detail** in this section is _____. **A:** Perhaps, the **most relevant supporting detail** in this section is _____.	• _____ justice, and opportunity given by those who _____ • Americans trade _____ for _____ to protect our democracy • we should be _____ for the America left to us, and leave a _____ _____ for those who follow us

 SUMMARIZE

"Shrink" Section 1 of the speech by writing a summary in 40 or fewer words.

CLASS SUMMARY: **WORD COUNT:** _____

As _____ we should recognize the _____

_____ we owe for our _____

and feel _____ for the _____

we inherited, while we attempt to improve it for _____

PARTNER SUMMARY: **WORD COUNT:** _____

We should have _____ for our _____

and should _____ to _____ and

_____ it so we can _____

a(n) _____ democracy.

 IDENTIFY PRECISE WORDS

Review Section 1 and your *Portfolio* (pp. 222–225) to identify words for your writing.

Topic Words	High-Utility Academic Words
• liberty • •	• gratitude • •

Words to Go

 BUILD WORD KNOWLEDGE

Complete the meanings and examples for these high-utility academic words.

Words to Go	Meanings	Examples
relevant rel·e·vant *adjective*	directly _____ _____ an issue or a matter	Mom told me that how I felt about _____ _____ _____ was not **relevant** to her decision.
relevance rel·e·vance *noun*	the condition of _____ an issue or a matter	Do _____ have **relevance** in this digital age?

💬 **DISCUSS & WRITE EXAMPLES**

Discuss your response with a partner. Then complete the sentence in writing.

It's important to include **relevant** _____

_____ when writing a justification or an argument essay.

Write your response and read it aloud to a partner.

The _____ of _____

_____ is clear when you consider how critical it is for college admissions.

📑 **BUILD WORD KNOWLEDGE**

Complete the meanings and examples for these high-utility academic words.

Words to Go	Meanings	Examples
responsive re·spon·sive *adjective*	_____ quickly and in a positive way	A good coach tries to be **responsive** to the _____ _____
responsiveness re·spon·sive·ness *noun*	the quality or state of _____ quickly and in a positive way	I was impressed by the **responsiveness** of the police when our community complained about _____ _____

💬 **DISCUSS & WRITE EXAMPLES**

Discuss your response with a partner. Then complete the sentence in writing.

A school administration should be especially **responsive** when it comes to important

issues like _____

Write your response and read it aloud to a partner.

The _____ of a live teacher is _____

_____ that conventional classrooms have over online courses.

Section Shrink

 BUILD FLUENCY
Read Section 2 of the speech "What Does It Mean to Be an American Citizen?"
(*Issues,* pp. 114–116).

 IDENTIFY KEY IDEAS & DETAILS
Take turns asking and answering questions with a partner. Then write brief notes.

Discussion Frames	Text Notes
Q: What is a **central idea** in this section? **A:** A **central idea** in this section is _____.	• creating a _____ government through _____
Q: What are the **relevant supporting details** in this section? **A:** (One/An additional) **relevant supporting detail** in this section is _____. **A:** Perhaps, the **most relevant supporting detail** in this section is _____.	• people are _____ less and _____ more • _____ leads to power-hungry _____; may destroy _____ • put aside _____ interests; instead take _____ to improve the _____

 SUMMARIZE
"Shrink" Section 2 of the speech by writing a summary in 40 or fewer words.

CLASS SUMMARY: **WORD COUNT:** _____

Without _____

such as _____ and putting aside

_____ to better support the common good,

_____ may fail.

PARTNER SUMMARY: **WORD COUNT:** _____

The _____ of American citizens threatens _____

and the _____ of our government, so we need to

_____ and attend to our _____

as we fight for the _____

 IDENTIFY PRECISE WORDS
Review Section 2 and your *Portfolio* (pp. 226–227) to identify words for your writing.

Topic Words	High-Utility Academic Words
• civic engagement • •	• endeavor • •

Words to Go

 BUILD WORD KNOWLEDGE

Complete the meanings and examples for these high-utility academic words.

Words to Go	Meanings	Examples
resolve re·solve *verb*	to find a _____ to a problem or to settle a _____	In order to **resolve** my transportation problems, I _____ _____
resolution res·o·lu·tion *noun*	an agreed-upon _____ to a problem	My sister and I are working toward a resolution of _____ _____

DISCUSS & WRITE EXAMPLES

Discuss your response with a partner. Then complete the sentence in writing.

My school **resolved** the problem of _____

_____ by starting the school day later.

Write your response and read it aloud to a partner.

It seems obvious that the best _____ to the high number of

_____ is to raise the driving age.

 BUILD WORD KNOWLEDGE

Complete the meaning and examples for this high-utility academic word.

Word to Go	Meaning	Examples
consensus con·sen·sus *noun*	an _____ among all the people in a group	It took a while, but my family finally reached a **consensus** on _____ _____ _____ There is a **consensus** among the students in Ms. Black's class that she is _____ _____

DISCUSS & WRITE EXAMPLES

Discuss your response with a partner. Then complete the sentence in writing.

The student body couldn't reach a decision about _____

_____ due to a lack of **consensus**.

Write your response and read it aloud to a partner.

The _____ of our class regarding school and job skills is that

_____

Section Shrink

 BUILD FLUENCY

Read Section 3 of the speech "What Does It Mean to Be an American Citizen?"
(*Issues*, pp. 116–121).

 IDENTIFY KEY IDEAS & DETAILS

Take turns asking and answering questions with a partner. Then write brief notes.

Discussion Frames	Text Notes
Q: What is a **central idea** in this section? **A:** A **central idea** in this section is _____.	• how citizens can _____ in democracy
Q: What are the **relevant supporting details** in this section? **A:** (One/An additional) **relevant supporting detail** in this section is _____. **A:** Perhaps, the **most relevant supporting detail** in this section is _____.	• most can't _____ big problems, but all can make _____ changes • citizens engage when they are informed about _____ and the _____ faced • _____ makes people feel like _____; helps them _____ democracy

 SUMMARIZE

"Shrink" Section 3 of the text by writing a summary in 40 or fewer words.

CLASS SUMMARY: **WORD COUNT:** _____

Most citizens will _____ to _____

small problems once they know _____

and doing so will _____

PARTNER SUMMARY: **WORD COUNT:** _____

People who _____ how their community works can

engage to _____

and, as a result, _____

as an integral part of the _____

IDENTIFY PRECISE WORDS

Review Section 3 and your *Portfolio* (pp. 228–229) to identify words for your writing.

Topic Words	High-Utility Academic Words
• constituent	• insignificant
•	•
•	•

Student Writing Model

Academic Writing Type

A **formal written summary** provides an objective overview of the topic and important details from an informational text. The writer credits the author, but writes in primarily his or her own words, without including personal opinions.

    A. The **topic sentence** includes the text type, title, author, and topic.
    B. **Detail sentences** include the important details from the summarized text.
    C. The **concluding sentence** restates the author's conclusion in the writer's own words.

⊕ ANALYZE TEXT

Read this student model to analyze the elements of a formal summary.

A

    In the op-ed article titled "Telling Americans to Vote, or Else," William A. Galston examines voting and citizenship. Galston begins

B

by suggesting that mandatory voting is a requirement that would improve our democracy. The writer continues to describe the dramatic increase to voter turnout in Australia after voting was changed from optional to mandatory. He discusses further that voting should be a civic responsibility for all American citizens, and that making voting mandatory would resolve the problem of policies that aren't representative of the entire citizenship. Moreover, the writer points out that a major incentive for making voting mandatory is that it would improve electoral politics and hold legislators accountable for their campaign promises. Galston concludes by emphasizing that mandatory

C

voting would force politicians to focus more on the issues and earn the trust of the Americans they represent.

MARK & DISCUSS ELEMENTS

Mark the summary elements and use the frames to discuss them with your partner.

1. **Number (1–4) the four elements of the topic sentence.**
   The topic sentence includes the _____.

2. **Draw a box around four transition words or phrases.**
   One transition (word/phrase) is _____.

3. **Underline four important details.** *One important detail in this summary is _____.*

4. **Circle four citation verbs.** *One citation verb that the writer uses is _____.*

5. **Star four precise topic words and check four high-utility academic words.**
   An example of a (precise topic word/high-utility academic word) is _____.

Organize a Formal Summary

| Prompt | Write a formal summary of "What Does It Mean to Be an American Citizen?" |

Guidelines for Paraphrasing Multiple Sentences

Paraphrase related details from a source text by combining key information into one sentence. Replace key words and phrases with synonyms and keep important topic words.

Text Detail 1	Text Detail 2	Text Detail 3
"People are voting less; paying less attention to their civic responsibility; ignoring the great lessons of the American experiment…" (Hamilton 114).	"There is a sense, particularly among many young people, that being an American citizen is no big deal, with no obligation attached to it…" (Hamilton 114).	"People think [elected representatives] are not relevant to their day-to-day lives" (Hamilton 114).

 PARAPHRASE IDEAS

Combine key information from the three text details above into one detail sentence.

Lack of understanding about the importance of democracy has led many Americans to

(Text Detail 1) _____

(Text Detail 2) _____ and

(Text Detail 3) _____

PLAN KEY IDEAS & DETAILS

State the text information to write a topic sentence.

In the speech titled (title) _____

(speaker's full name) _____

(citation verb: presents, investigates, discusses) _____

(topic) _____

List four important details from the text using primarily your own words.

1. _____

    _____

2. _____

    _____

3. _____

    _____

4. _____

    _____

Restate the conclusion in your own words.

_____

_____

Write a Formal Summary

Prompt | Write a formal summary of "What Does It Mean to Be an American Citizen?"

✏️ **WRITE A PARAGRAPH**
Use the frame to write your topic sentence, detail sentences, and concluding sentence.

A

In the _____ titled _____
    (text type)   (title)

_____   _____
(speaker's full name)   (citation verb)

(topic)
_____

B

_____ begins by _____
(Speaker's last name)   (citation verb + -ing: presenting, arguing)

(1st important detail)
_____

_____

_____

The speaker continues to _____
                                (citation verb, base form: describe, report)

(2nd important detail)
_____

_____

_____

(He/She) _____ _____ further that
             (present-tense citation verb)

(3rd important detail)
_____

_____

_____

Moreover, the speaker _____
                       (present-tense citation verb)

(4th important detail)
_____

_____

_____

C

_____ concludes by _____
(Speaker's last name)   (citation verb + -ing: suggesting, emphasizing)

(restate conclusion)
_____

_____

Rate Your Summary

ASSESS YOUR DRAFT

Rate your formal summary. Then have a partner rate it.

Scoring Guide	
1	Insufficient
2	Developing
3	Sufficient
4	Exemplary

1. Does the topic sentence state the title, speaker, and topic?	Self	1	2	3	4
	Partner	1	2	3	4
2. Did you paraphrase the most important details from the speech?	Self	1	2	3	4
	Partner	1	2	3	4
3. Did you use citation verbs to credit the speaker?	Self	1	2	3	4
	Partner	1	2	3	4
4. Did you use transitions to introduce and sequence details?	Self	1	2	3	4
	Partner	1	2	3	4
5. Did you include precise topic words and high-utility academic words?	Self	1	2	3	4
	Partner	1	2	3	4
6. Did you restate the speaker's conclusion using your own words?	Self	1	2	3	4
	Partner	1	2	3	4

REFLECT & REVISE

Record specific priorities and suggestions to help you and your partner revise.

(Partner) Positive Feedback: I appreciate how you (used/included) _____

_____

_____

(Partner) Suggestion: As you revise your summary, focus on _____

_____

_____

(Self) Priority 1: My summary paragraph needs _____

_____

_____

(Self) Priority 2: I plan to improve my summary by _____

_____

CHECK & EDIT

Use this checklist to proofread and edit your summary.

☐ Did you capitalize the title of the speech and proper nouns?

☐ Did you put quotation marks around the title of the speech?

☐ Did you use commas appropriately after transitions?

☐ Do simple present-tense verbs end in –s?

☐ Is each sentence complete?

☐ Are all words spelled correctly?

Words to Know

 BUILD WORD KNOWLEDGE
Rate your word knowledge. Then discuss word meanings and examples with your group.

		① Don't Know	② Recognize	③ Familiar	④ Know

Word to Know	Meaning	Examples
1 **registered** *adjective* ① ② ③ ④	entered or recorded on an _____ list	As a **registered** student in a college-level class, I have access to _____ _____ _____ My mother had to pass a licensing exam to become a **registered** _____ _____
2 **organize** *verb* ① ② ③ ④	to _____ _____ and manage an event or an activity	The prom committee will **organize** a _____ to help pay for the event. For Mother's Day, I **organized** a _____ _____ _____ for my mom.
3 **eliminate** *verb* ① ② ③ ④	to completely _____ _____ an unnecessary or _____ item	Using _____ can **eliminate** the need for paper maps. Our school **eliminated** _____ _____ from the lunch menu so students would have healthier choices.
4 **barrier** *noun* ① ② ③ ④	a rule or a problem that _____ or limits people from doing something	_____ _____ was a **barrier** to my attendance at the after-school picnic in the park. After we _____ _____ I had to work hard to break down the **barriers** between _____ _____ and me.

Close Reading

 READ THE TEXT

Read the excerpt from *Countdown* (*Issues*, pp. 122–129).

IDENTIFY KEY IDEAS & DETAILS

Use the frames to analyze the text and make inferences.

1. The author writes: "After three tries, Fannie successfully registered to vote." What can you infer about Fannie's character based on this text evidence?

   The fact that Fannie _____

   the first three times suggests that _____

   _____

   This reveals that Fannie was _____ because she

   _____

ANALYZE CRAFT & STRUCTURE

Use the frames to analyze the author's use of literary devices.

Literary Devices

Literary devices are the methods and techniques authors use to convey their messages in literary texts. **Irony** is a literary device that contrasts what happens in a text with what the reader might expect to happen. **Mood** is the effect that a writer's words have on readers. The mood of a text describes how the writer's words make readers feel.

2. Why does the author point out some of the significant events of 1961, the year that Fannie learns she can vote?

   The author points out some of the significant events of 1961 to _____

   _____

   and to contrast _____

   with _____

   _____

3. How do the five indented lines on page 127 reflect the author's use of irony?

   The lines are ironic because the first four lines describe _____

   _____ but the last line lets

   the reader know that, in fact, the actions had the _____ effect

   and _____

4. What mood does the author create with the words *arrested, beaten, ridiculed,* and *shot at*? How does the mood change when the author uses the word *galvanized*?

   These words convey a mood of _____

   Because the word _____ suggests

   _____ the mood shifts from one of

   _____ to one of _____

Academic Discussion
How do citizens today perceive voting differently than those in the past?

BRAINSTORM IDEAS

Briefly record at least two ideas in each column using everyday English.

In the Past	In the Present
• a right	• a hassle
•	•
•	•

ANALYZE WORDS

Complete the chart with precise words to discuss and write about the topic.

Everyday	Precise
right *(noun)*	prerogative,
change *(verb)*	alter,
choose *(verb)*	elect,

MAKE A CLAIM

Rewrite two ideas using the frames and precise words. Then prepare to elaborate verbally.

Language to ELABORATE

To clarify, _____.

Based on my experience, _____.

1. **Frame:** Some citizens today view voting as _____ (**adjective:** inconvenient, corrupt, insignificant), whereas citizens in the past viewed voting as a(n) _____ (**noun:** obligation, duty, right)

   Response: _____

   _____

2. **Frame:** For Fannie Lou Hamer, voting was a way to _____ (**base verb:** have, fight, affect)

   Response: _____

   _____

COLLABORATE

Listen attentively, restate, and record your partner's ideas.

Language to RESTATE

In other words, your point of view is that _____.

Yes, that's accurate.

No. What I intended to say was _____.

Classmate's Name	Ideas
	1.
	2.

Ten-Minute Paper

A **ten-minute paper** begins with a **claim,** followed by **two detail sentences** that elaborate with relevant examples and precise words.

Language to COMPARE IDEAS

My point of view on _____ is (similar to/somewhat different from) _____'s.

 PRESENT IDEAS

Listen, compare ideas, and take notes. Then indicate if you agree (+) or disagree (−).

Classmate's Name	Idea	+/−

ELABORATE IN WRITING

Work with the teacher to write a ten-minute paper.

Language to COLLABORATE

What should we write? We could select _____.

What do you think is a strong selection?

As an alternative, we could write _____.

Some citizens today view voting as an inconvenience, whereas citizens in the past viewed voting as a privilege. For example, it is often time-consuming to _____ _____ especially when _____

As a result, many people _____

because they _____

or they _____

_____

Work with a partner to write a ten-minute paper.

For Fannie Lou Hamer, voting was a way to _____

_____

For example, _____

_____

_____

As a result, _____

_____

Take a Stand

Debate | Should the United States implement compulsory voting?

 COLLABORATE
Read the debate question about voting. Then take turns using a frame to respond with your initial reaction.

Language to RESPOND

So _____, what's your initial reaction?

My initial reaction is _____.

My initial reaction is related to _____'s.

ANALYZE SOURCES
Read a quote that either supports or opposes the debate question. Then paraphrase.

Quote	Paraphrase
Model: "If American citizens increasingly become disengaged, then the entire American democratic enterprise is at risk" (Hamilton 114–115).	This quote makes it evident that our _____ will be _____ if citizens aren't _____ in our government.
1. "Requiring people to vote in national elections once every two years would reinforce the principle of reciprocity at the heart of citizenship" (Galston 108).	The author seems to be saying that even demanding _____ in national elections is a responsibility of _____ that counters the _____ provided by the government.
2. "Mandatory voting would tend to even out disparities stemming from income, education and age, enhancing our system's inclusiveness" (Galston 109).	This quote makes it evident that making voting _____ would result in more balanced _____ of voters, despite their different _____ _____
3. "Mandating voting nationwide would go counter to our traditions (and perhaps our Constitution) and would encounter strong state opposition" (Galston 111).	This quote makes it evident that many states would _____ mandatory voting, because it goes against American _____ and maybe even _____
4. "You and I are concerned because we know that if we are apathetic, passive, and cynical about our democracy, then we will invite leaders who abuse power" (Hamilton 114).	The author seems to be saying that if Americans don't _____ our _____ then corrupt _____ may be elected.

Debate Ideas

 SYNTHESIZE IDEAS

Write a response to the debate question, including a paraphrase of a text quote and elaboration on the quote.

Claim: My position is that the United States (should/should not) _____

_____ implement compulsory voting.

Transitional Statement: I have (one key reason/a compelling reason) _____

_____ for taking this stance.

Quote Paraphrase: (For example,/According to (author),) _____.

_____

_____

_____

Quote Elaboration: (As a result,/Consequently,) _____.

_____

_____

_____

PRESENT EVIDENCE

Using Gestures for Emphasis

When presenting ideas during class or in a meeting, use **gestures for emphasis.** Move your hands when you make an important point or present a surprising piece of evidence.

LISTEN & TAKE NOTES

Listen attentively and take notes. Then indicate if you agree (+) or disagree (–).

Language to AFFIRM & CLARIFY

I can understand why you see it this way.
Could you explain what you mean by _____?

Classmate's Name	Idea	+/–

Student Writing Model

Academic Writing Type

An **argument** states a claim and supports it with logical reasons and relevant evidence from sources.

 A. The **thesis statement** clearly states the writer's claim and tells what the writer will explain about the topic.
 B. **Supporting paragraphs** support the claim with reasons and evidence from sources. The writer also presents counterclaims and responds with strong evidence.
 C. The **conclusion statement** restates the writer's claim about the issue.

ANALYZE TEXT

Read this student model to analyze elements of an argument research paper.

A After examining the issues surrounding voting and citizenship, I am convinced that the United States should not implement compulsory voting.

B One reason I maintain this position is that many people are likely to rebel against voting if it's presented as an obligation. In "Telling Americans to Vote, or Else," William A. Galston emphasizes that when Australia made voting mandatory, some feared that spite would be an incentive to destroy ballots (108). As a teen, I have firsthand experience with actions fueled by spite. As an illustration, when we were forced to wear school uniforms, organizers staged a protest in which students cut off their sleeves and pant legs. In contrast, proponents of mandatory voting believe that it would resolve the problem of apathy among American citizens (Galston 108). However, I am not convinced that forcing people to vote would make them more responsive.

The Honorable Lee H. Hamilton's analysis of American citizenship and the institution of democracy in "What Does It Mean to Be an American Citizen?" has strengthened my perspective that compulsory voting is a fruitless effort. According to Hamilton, many Americans believe that elected officials are the puppets of interest groups rather than the people (114). Although a common argument in favor of compulsory voting is that it would give typically underrepresented voters a greater voice in government (Galston 109), I don't find the evidence compelling. Clearly, there is adequate evidence that shows that those are the people who would be least able to pay the fines imposed if they failed to turn up to vote (Galston 109).

C The question of whether or not to make voting mandatory is provocative. My analysis of this issue has left me with little doubt that compulsory voting should not be implemented in the United States.

MARK & DISCUSS ELEMENTS

Mark the argument elements and use the frames to discuss them with your partner.

1. **Circle the writer's claim within the thesis statement.** *The writer's claim is _____.*

2. **Underline and label two reasons that support the writer's claim with the letter *R*.** *One reason that supports the writer's claim is _____.*

3. **Underline and label four pieces of evidence that support the writer's claim with the letter *E*.** *One piece of evidence that supports the writer's claim is _____.*

4. **Draw boxes around two counterclaims.** *One counterclaim is _____.*

5. **Star four precise topic words and check four high-utility academic words.** *An example of a (precise topic word/high-utility academic word) is _____.*

ASSESS A STUDENT SAMPLE
Read an additional student model and rate it.

Scoring Guide			
1	Insufficient	3	Sufficient
2	Developing	4	Exemplary

1. Does the thesis statement clearly state the claim?	1	2	3	4
2. Do supporting paragraphs begin with a topic sentence that specifies a reason?	1	2	3	4
3. Did the writer give evidence drawn primarily from sources to support the claim?	1	2	3	4
4. Did the writer explain why the evidence is relevant and significant?	1	2	3	4
5. Did the writer include complex sentences to present and respond to counterclaims?	1	2	3	4
6. Did the writer use strong verbs and verb phrases to express opinions?	1	2	3	4
7. Did the writer use transitions to introduce reasons and evidence?	1	2	3	4
8. Did the writer use precise adjectives to describe evidence?	1	2	3	4
9. Did the writer include citation information for text evidence?	1	2	3	4
10. Did the writer include precise topic words and high-utility words?	1	2	3	4
11. Does the conclusion statement strongly restate the claim using new wording?	1	2	3	4

REFLECT & REVISE
Record specific priorities and suggestions to help the writer.

The writer did an effective job of (organizing/including/stating) _____

_____

_____

One way the writer could make the argument stronger is _____

_____

_____

I noticed that the writer (forgot to/included/used) _____

_____

_____

This will support me with writing an argument because I will remember to _____

_____

_____

Verbs and Verb Phrases to Express Opinion

Opinion	Verbs/Verb Phrases to Express an Opinion	Argument Examples
agree	*believe, conclude, contend, support, maintain, concur* *agree wholeheartedly that* *still maintain that* *still contend that* *am convinced that*	After examining the issues surrounding citizenship and voting, I **believe** that voting should be mandatory. One reason I **am convinced that** Americans will reject mandatory voting is that it may be unconstitutional.
disagree	*contend, reject, maintain, challenge, conclude, oppose* *disagree entirely that* *cannot support the opinion that* *am not convinced that*	However, I **reject** that Americans would deliberately destroy ballots. One reason I **still contend that** politicians would work harder is that they would have to please more voters.
undecided	*am uncertain, am unsure, am unconvinced, hesitate* *am undecided about whether* *see both sides of the issue* *am more inclined to believe*	Although the text includes some interesting evidence, I **am unsure** that voting should be compulsory. Due to the evidence presented, I **see both sides of the issue.**

IDENTIFY VERB PHRASES

Circle the verbs and verb phrases in the chart that you plan to use in your argument. Then complete each sentence with a verb or verb phrase to express an opinion.

1. After reviewing the evidence, I _____ more Americans should participate in local politics.

2. Despite the evidence presented, I _____ mandatory voting would lessen the power of special interests.

3. For these reasons, I _____ that civic engagement will improve with compulsory voting.

WRITE OPINIONS

Write sentences that express the opinion in parentheses. Include details from texts.

1. **(agree)** After analyzing the research on citizenship and voting, I _____
   _____

2. **(disagree)** However, I _____
   _____

3. **(undecided)** Although the article presents interesting evidence, I _____
   _____

Present Perfect-Tense Verbs

Guidelines for Using Present Perfect-Tense Verbs

Present perfect-tense verbs show action that happened sometime in the past or action that has happened and is still happening. Use present perfect-tense verbs to provide data and anecdotal evidence from the text or your experience that supports your claim.

I **have heard** people who don't vote complaining about the government.	hear → have heard
Studies **have shown** that voters are more involved citizens.	show → have shown
My uncle **has voted** in every election, but still feels unrepresented.	vote → has voted
Research **has proven** that voter turnout in Australia is near 95%.	prove → has proven

 IDENTIFY PRESENT PERFECT TENSE

Read the paragraph from an argument and circle the present perfect-tense verbs.

> After examining the issues surrounding voter turnout, I am convinced that same-day registration is the solution to the challenge of motivating voters to go to the polls.
>
> One reason I maintain this position is that people may decide at the last minute that they want to vote. In "Same-Day Registration," Marion Just emphasizes that people who have shown little interest in voting may be tempted to cast a ballot after they have witnessed two weeks of intense campaign ads leading up to Election Day (1). As a teen, I have firsthand experience with deciding to do something at the last minute. As an illustration, I have applied for a spot in a summer internship just before the deadline, because I could do so online. In contrast, some people I know have claimed that last-minute voters aren't well informed. However, I reject that notion because those voters have reacted strongly enough to something in the campaign ads to make them get out and vote.

 WRITE PRESENT PERFECT-TENSE VERBS

Complete the sentences with the present perfect tense of the verbs in parentheses.

1. Australia (mandate) _____ compulsory voting since 1924.

2. Laws there (yield) _____ voting by almost 95% of citizens, with only the threat of small fines for nonvoters.

3. The law (establish) _____ permissible excuses for not voting, like illness or travel out of the country.

4. The laws (change) _____ the way people in Australia feel about voting.

Organize an Argument

Prompt | Should the United States implement compulsory voting? Write an argument that states your claim and supports it with text evidence.

Guidelines for Citing Text Evidence

Paraphrase text evidence when you want to summarize a longer section of text or multiple ideas. Use **direct quotes** when the author has used strong wording that is difficult to improve or simplify.

Quote	Paraphrase or Incorporate Quote
"The law also changed civic norms. Australians are more likely than before to see voting as an obligation." (Galston 108).	In "Telling Americans to Vote, or Else," William Galston emphasizes that mandatory voting in Australia transformed voting into a civic duty (108).
"…an endeavor not particularly worthy of their time and talent" (Hamilton 114)	Young people feel that American citizenship, of which voting is an integral part, is "an endeavor not particularly worthy of their time and talent" (Hamilton 114).

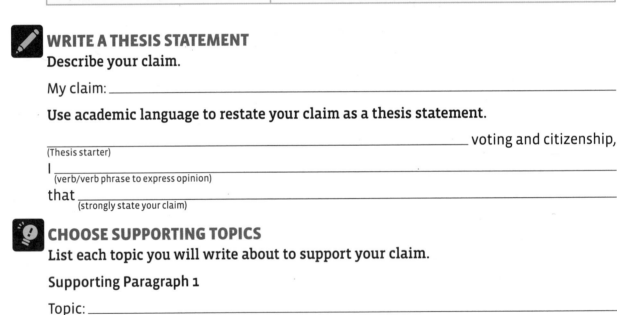

✏️ **WRITE A THESIS STATEMENT**
Describe your claim.

My claim: _____

Use academic language to restate your claim as a thesis statement.

_____ voting and citizenship,
(Thesis starter)

I _____
(verb/verb phrase to express opinion)

that _____
(strongly state your claim)

💡 **CHOOSE SUPPORTING TOPICS**
List each topic you will write about to support your claim.

Supporting Paragraph 1

Topic: _____

_____

Supporting Paragraph 2

Topic: _____

_____

Find text evidence that supports your claim and write a sentence that paraphrases it or incorporates a direct quote.

_____

_____

_____

📄 PLAN SUPPORTING PARAGRAPHS

List reasons and evidence that support your claim. You may draw from texts, your experience, or a classmate's experience.

Supporting Paragraph 1:

Reason 1: _____

_____

Evidence: _____

_____

_____

Source/Page Number: _____

Author: _____

Counterclaim 1: _____

_____

Response to Counterclaim: _____

_____

Source/Page Number: _____

Author: _____

Supporting Paragraph 2:

Reason 2: _____

_____

Evidence: _____

_____

_____

Source/Page Number: _____

Author: _____

Counterclaim 2: _____

_____

Response to Counterclaim: _____

_____

Source/Page Number: _____

Author: _____

✏️ WRITE A CONCLUSION

Write a conclusion statement that restates your claim.

The question of whether or not to _____
(restate the issue)

is _____ My analysis of this issue has left me with little
(precise adjective to respond)

doubt that _____
(restate your claim)

_____

Write an Argument

Prompt Should the United States implement compulsory voting? Write an argument that states your claim and supports it with text evidence.

 WRITE A RESEARCH PAPER
Use the frame to write your thesis statement, supporting paragraphs, and conclusion statement.

A

_____
(Thesis starter)

_____
(topic)

I _____
(verb/verb phrase to express opinion)

that _____
(strongly state your claim)

_____

B1

One reason I maintain this position is that _____
(1st reason that supports your claim)

_____

_____

In _____
(title of source)

_____ emphasizes that
(author's full name)

_____
(evidence from source)

_____

_____

As a teen, I have firsthand experience with _____
(situation or issue)

_____

_____ _____
(Transition introducing evidence)   (evidence from your experience)

_____

In contrast, _____
(group with an opposing claim)

_____ that _____
(verb/verb phrase to express opinion)   (counterclaim from source or your experience)

_____

However, I _____ that _____
(verb/verb phrase to express opinion)   (your response to the counterclaim)

_____

_____

_____ analysis of _____
(Author's full name + 's)   (topic)

_____

in _____
   (title of a different source)

has strengthened my perspective that _____
                                     (2nd reason that supports your claim)

_____

_____

_____   _____
(Transition introducing evidence)   (evidence from source or your experience)

_____

_____

_____

B2 Although a common argument (in favor of/against) _____

_____
(issue)

is _____
   (counterclaim from source or your experience)

_____

_____

_____

I don't find the evidence (compelling/substantial/believable) _____

Clearly, there is (sufficient/adequate/striking) _____

evidence that (shows/proves) _____
                             (your response to the counterclaim)

_____

_____

The question of whether or not to _____
                                   (restate the issue)

_____

is _____ My analysis of this issue has left me with little
   (precise adjective to respond)

C doubt that _____
                  (restate your claim)

_____

_____

IS FAILURE THE SECRET OF SUCCESS?

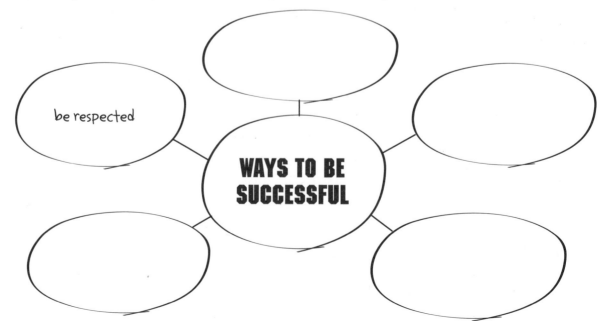

BUILD KNOWLEDGE
Read and respond to the Data File (*Issues*, p. 130).

BRAINSTORM IDEAS
Write a brief list of ways that people can be considered successful.

- *do well in school* _____
- _____
- _____
- _____

PRESENT IDEAS
Use the frames to discuss ideas with your group. Listen attentively and record the strongest ideas to complete the concept map.

Language to FACILITATE DISCUSSION

So, _____, what's your suggestion?

_____, what example did you come up with?

1. One way to be considered successful is to _____ (**base verb**: excel)

2. Successful people tend to _____ (**base verb**: earn)

3. Another sign of success is to _____ (**base verb**: form)

4. A truly successful person can _____ (**base verb**: create)

be respected

WAYS TO BE SUCCESSFUL

Words to Know

BUILD WORD KNOWLEDGE

Rate your word knowledge. Then discuss word meanings and examples with your group.

| | ① Don't Know | ② Recognize | ③ Familiar | ④ Know |

Word to Know	Meaning	Examples
1 **achievement** *noun* ① ② ③ ④	an important result that is _____ by _____	When I finally _____ _____ I was proud of my **achievement**.
2 **criticism** *noun* ① ② ③ ④	remarks that say what you think is _____ about someone or something	I appreciate thoughtful **criticism** when _____ _____ _____ _____
3 **challenging** *adjective* ① ② ③ ④	_____ but also interesting or _____	_____ _____ _____ was **challenging**, but I found it satisfying.
4 **determined** *adjective* ① ② ③ ④	having a strong _____ to do something and not letting anything _____ you	This year at school, I am **determined** to _____ _____ _____ _____
1 **trait** *noun* ① ② ③ ④	a _____ that makes someone or something _____	One of the most important **traits** for a friend to have is _____ _____
2 **grit** *noun* ① ② ③ ④	_____ or determination shown in a _____ situation	By _____ _____ _____ Azealia really showed her **grit**.
3 **obstacle** *noun* ① ② ③ ④	something that makes it _____ to do something	I _____ _____ _____ about people who overcame many **obstacles**.
4 **persevere** *verb* ① ② ③ ④	to continue _____ to do something	I know that if I **persevere** with my _____ _____ I will like the results.

Academic Discussion
What are the traits of people who succeed and people who fail?

 BRAINSTORM IDEAS

Briefly record at least two ideas in each column using everyday English.

Succeed	Fail
• brave	• bored
•	•
•	•

 ANALYZE WORDS

Complete the chart with precise words to discuss and write about the topic.

Everyday	Precise
hard-working *(adjective)*	enterprising,
put off *(verb)*	postpone,
scared *(adjective)*	unwilling,

 MAKE A CLAIM

Rewrite two ideas using the frames and precise words. Then prepare to elaborate verbally.

> **Language to ELABORATE**
>
> To exemplify, _____.
>
> Personally, _____.

1. **Frame:** In my experience, people who (succeed/fail) are _____ (**adjective:** persistent, unintelligent) and _____ (**adjective:** resilient, untalented).

   Response: _____

   _____

2. **Frame:** From my perspective, people (succeed/fail) because they _____ (**present-tense verb:** persevere, try, lack)

   Response: _____

   _____

 COLLABORATE

Listen attentively, restate, and record your partner's idea.

> **Language to RESTATE**
>
> In other words, your stance is that _____.
>
> Yes, that's accurate.
>
> No. What I intended to say was _____.

Classmate's Name	Ideas
	1.
	2.

Ten-Minute Paper

A **ten-minute paper** begins with a **claim,** followed by **two detail sentences** that elaborate with relevant examples and precise words.

 PRESENT IDEAS

Listen, compare ideas, and take notes. Then indicate if you agree (+) or disagree (–).

Classmate's Name	Idea	+/–

ELABORATE IN WRITING

Work with a partner to write a ten-minute paper.

In my experience, people who succeed are motivated and ambitious. For example, when people start careers they have _____ they are more likely to be enthusiastic about _____ _____

As a result, they become _____ _____

Write a ten-minute paper.

From my perspective, people _____ because they _____ _____

For example, when faced with _____

people might decide not to risk _____

As a result, they never _____

or find out _____

Words to Go

 BUILD WORD KNOWLEDGE

Complete the meaning and examples for this high-utility academic word.

Word to Go	Meaning	Examples
evolve e·volve *verb*	to _____ slowly over a _____ period of time	_____ _____ (is/are) an example of how technology continues to **evolve**. During high school, I expect that my _____ _____ will **evolve**.

 DISCUSS & WRITE EXAMPLES

Discuss your response with a partner. Then complete the sentence in writing.

The baseball team has **evolved** by _____

_____

Write your response and read it aloud to a partner.

The popularity of _____

is proof that our education system is _____

 BUILD WORD KNOWLEDGE

Complete the meanings and examples for these high-utility academic words.

Words to Go	Meanings	Examples
emphasize em·pha·size *verb*	to draw _____ to something	At every practice, our coach **emphasizes** the need for _____ _____
emphasis em·pha·sis *noun*	_____ put on something	Our teacher explained that the test would have an **emphasis** on _____ _____ _____

 DISCUSS & WRITE EXAMPLES

Discuss your response with a partner. Then complete the sentence in writing.

Recent studies have **emphasized** the connection between _____

_____ and driving.

Write your response and read it aloud to a partner.

Vocational schools place an _____ on _____

_____

Close Reading

BUILD FLUENCY
Read the text "Talent Isn't Fixed and Other Mindsets That Lead to Greatness"
(*Issues*, pp. 131–135).

IDENTIFY KEY IDEAS & DETAILS
Take turns asking and answering questions with a partner. Then write brief notes.

Discussion Frames	Text Notes
Q: What is a **central idea** in this text? A: A **central idea** in this text is _____.	• hard work and effort can develop _____
Q: What are the **relevant supporting details** in this text? A: (One/An additional) **relevant supporting detail** in this text is _____.	• people with a _____ are afraid of _____ • feedback should focus on the _____, not the _____ • people can develop a _____ by seeing _____ and _____ as opportunities

RESPOND WITH EVIDENCE
Use the frames and evidence from the text to construct a formal written response.

1. According to the text, how do the two mindsets affect "dealing with setbacks"?

   According to the text, people with growth mindsets view setbacks as _____

   _____

   whereas people with fixed mindsets view setbacks as _____

   _____

   Use the frame to analyze the interview's text structure.

2. How does the interviewer use question 3 to follow up on information the interviewee
   provides in the previous question?

   In question 2, the interviewee defines _____

   and explains how they affect _____

   In question 3, the interviewer follows up by asking the interviewee how the mindsets

   _____

IDENTIFY PRECISE WORDS
Review Text 1 and your *Portfolio* (pp. 248–253) to identify words for your writing.

Topic Words	High-Utility Academic Words
• growth mindset	• endless
•	•
•	•

Academic Discussion

What are the differences between a fixed mindset and a growth mindset?

 BRAINSTORM IDEAS

Briefly record at least two ideas in each column using everyday English.

Fixed Mindset	Growth Mindset
• new things are scary	• mistakes something to learn from
•	•
•	•

 ANALYZE WORDS

Complete the chart with precise words to discuss and write about the issue.

Everyday	Precise
slipup *(noun)*	error,
decide *(verb)*	judge,
new *(adjective)*	untried,

 MAKE A CLAIM

Rewrite two ideas using the frames and precise words. Then prepare to elaborate verbally.

> **Language to ELABORATE**
>
> To exemplify, _____.
>
> Personally, _____.

1. **Frame:** People with a fixed mindset tend to _____ (**base verb:** think, consider, give up), whereas people with a growth mindset are more likely to _____ (**base verb:** persist, apply, learn)

   Response: _____

   _____

2. **Frame:** A person with a fixed mindset often _____ (**present-tense verb:** attributes, chooses, feels) while a person with a growth mindset _____ (**present-tense verb:** develops, achieves, focuses)

   Response: _____

   _____

 COLLABORATE

Listen attentively, restate, and record your partner's ideas.

> **Language to RESTATE**
>
> In other words, your stance is that _____.
>
> Yes, that's accurate.
>
> No. What I intended to say was _____.

Classmate's Name	Ideas
	1.
	2.

Ten-Minute Paper

A **ten-minute paper** begins with a **claim,** followed by **two detail sentences** that elaborate with relevant examples and precise words.

 PRESENT IDEAS

Listen, compare ideas, and take notes. Then indicate if you agree (+) or disagree (–).

Classmate's Name	Idea	+/–

ELABORATE IN WRITING

Work with a partner to write a ten-minute paper.

People with a fixed mindset tend to feel that talent is limited, whereas people with a growth mindset are more likely to view talent as a skill that can evolve through effort. For example, someone with a growth mindset will _____

_____

As a result, the _____ become more _____

_____ and the _____ gains _____

_____

Write a ten-minute paper.

A person with a fixed mindset often _____

_____ while a person with a growth mindset

_____

For example, people with fixed mindsets attribute failures to _____

_____ but people with growth mindsets treat failure

_____

As a result, those with growth mindsets _____

_____

Words to Go

 BUILD WORD KNOWLEDGE

Complete the meaning and examples for this high-utility academic word.

Word to Go	Meaning	Examples
compensate com·pen·sate *verb*	to _____ or _____ for something	To **compensate** for forgetting my friend's birthday, I _____ _____ Our teacher _____ _____ to **compensate** for our final exam preparations.

💬 **DISCUSS & WRITE EXAMPLES**

Discuss your response with a partner. Then complete the sentence in writing.

Teens who stay up late sometimes **compensate** for their lack of sleep by _____

_____ the next day.

Write your response and read it aloud to a partner.

After being out sick for several weeks last year, I _____ for the

schoolwork I missed by _____

 BUILD WORD KNOWLEDGE

Complete the meanings and examples for these high-utility academic words.

Words to Go	Meanings	Examples
predictive pre·dict·ive *adjective*	having to do with the ability to show what will happen in the _____	My smartphone uses **predictive** typing; _____ _____ _____
predictor pre·dic·tor *noun*	something that shows what will _____ in the future	My brother's hyperactivity in elementary school was not a **predictor** of his _____ in high school.

💬 **DISCUSS & WRITE EXAMPLES**

Discuss your response with a partner. Then complete the sentence in writing.

How teens _____

is not necessarily **predictive** of how they will act as adults.

Write your response and read it aloud to a partner.

Political polls are only sometimes accurate _____ of

_____

Section Shrink

 BUILD FLUENCY

Read Section 1 of "Angela Duckworth and the Research on 'Grit'" (*Issues,* pp. 136–137).

 IDENTIFY KEY IDEAS & DETAILS

Take turns asking and answering questions with a partner. Then write brief notes.

Discussion Frames	Text Notes
Q: What is a **central idea** in this section? **A:** A **central idea** in this section is _____.	• the relationship between _____ and _____
Q: What are the **relevant supporting details** in this section? **A:** (One/An additional) **relevant supporting detail** in this section is _____. **A:** Perhaps the **most relevant supporting detail** in this section is _____.	• grit is the ability to _____ _____ something until you become _____ • _____ can compensate for lower _____ • students with more _____ have the best _____ • professor Angela Duckworth developed a _____

 SUMMARIZE

"Shrink" Section 1 of the article by writing a summary in 40 or fewer words.

CLASS SUMMARY   **WORD COUNT:** _____

People with _____ are extremely _____

which causes them to _____ and can influence _____

_____ even more than _____

PARTNER SUMMARY   **WORD COUNT:** _____

_____ and _____ are indicators

of _____ which may impact a person's _____

as much as, if not more than, _____

Ⓠ IDENTIFY PRECISE WORDS

Review Section 1 and your *Portfolio* (pp. 254–257) to identify words for your writing.

Topic Words	High-Utility Academic Words
• personality trait	• master
•	•
•	•

Words to Go

 BUILD WORD KNOWLEDGE

Complete the meanings and examples for these high-utility academic words.

Words to Go	Meanings	Examples
ultimate ul·ti·mate *adjective*	_____ ; happening at the _____ of a process	I am going to graduate high school, but my **ultimate** goal is to _____ _____ _____
ultimately ul·ti·mate·ly *adverb*	_____ ; after everything has been done	After a difficult, but **ultimately** triumphant season, our coach _____ _____

 DISCUSS & WRITE EXAMPLES

Discuss your response with a partner. Then complete the sentence in writing.

The **ultimate** aim of _____

is to prepare students for work.

Write your response and read it aloud to a partner.

_____ each individual must practice responsibility and become

_____

 BUILD WORD KNOWLEDGE

Complete the meanings and examples for these high-utility academic words.

Words to Go	Meaning	Examples
intervene in·ter·vene *verb*	to get _____ in a _____ situation	When my sisters were arguing, I had to **intervene** so that they wouldn't _____ _____
intervention in·ter·ven·tion *noun*	an action taken to _____ a difficult situation	Without **intervention**, some students might _____ _____

DISCUSS & WRITE EXAMPLES

Discuss your response with a partner. Then complete the sentence in writing.

If you know someone who is _____

because of credit cards, you should consider **intervening**.

Write your response and read it aloud to a partner.

Not allowing teens to drive at night is an _____ meant to decrease

_____

Section Shrink

 BUILD FLUENCY

Read Section 2 of "Angela Duckworth and the Research on 'Grit'" (*Issues*, pp. 137–141).

IDENTIFY KEY IDEAS & DETAILS

Take turns asking and answering questions with a partner. Then write brief notes.

Discussion Frames	Text Notes
Q: What is a **central idea** in this section? **A:** A **central idea** in this section is _____.	• _____ is an important factor in _____
Q: What are the **relevant supporting details** in this section? **A:** (One/An additional) **relevant supporting detail** in this section is _____. **A:** Perhaps the **most relevant supporting detail** in this section is _____.	• some _____ charter school students get into _____ but don't _____ • _____ students face the _____ of college with fewer _____ • grit can help students overcome _____ such as _____

✏️ **SUMMARIZE**

"Shrink" Section 2 of the article by writing a summary in 40 or fewer words.

CLASS SUMMARY   **WORD COUNT:** _____

Duckworth has observed how _____ affects _____

_____ who graduate from college

despite _____

such as _____

PARTNER SUMMARY   **WORD COUNT:** _____

_____ college students need _____

than students from _____ families

to _____ challenges and _____

 IDENTIFY PRECISE WORDS

Review Section 2 and your *Portfolio* (pp. 258–259) to identify words for your writing.

Topic Words	High-Utility Academic Words
• charter school	• barriers
•	•
•	•

Words to Go

 BUILD WORD KNOWLEDGE

Complete the meanings and examples for these high-utility academic words.

Words to Go	Meanings	Examples
environment en·vi·ron·ment *noun*	the _____ and _____ that surround and affect someone	The **environment** at the library is too quiet for me, so I usually do my homework at _____ _____
environmental en·vi·ron·men·tal *adjective*	concerning the _____ and _____ around someone	_____ _____ can be an **environmental** threat in cities.

 DISCUSS & WRITE EXAMPLES

Discuss your response with a partner. Then complete the sentence in writing.

Some people believe that _____

provide a more supportive **environment** than online courses.

Write your response and read it aloud to a partner.

_____ factors such as _____

can contribute to teens' lack of sleep.

BUILD WORD KNOWLEDGE

Complete the meaning and examples for this high-utility academic word.

Word to Go	Meaning	Examples
confront con·front *verb*	to _____ with a _____ ; to appear and cause _____	I hope that the challenges that **confront** me in college don't include _____ _____ My parents need to **confront** my brother about his habit of _____ _____

DISCUSS & WRITE EXAMPLES

Discuss your response with a partner. Then complete the sentence in writing.

I would have to **confront** a friend who _____

_____

Write your response and read it aloud to a partner.

Online courses may _____ students with tempting opportunities

to _____

Section Shrink

 BUILD FLUENCY

Read Section 3 of "Angela Duckworth and the Research on 'Grit'" (*Issues*, pp. 141–143).

 IDENTIFY KEY IDEAS & DETAILS

Take turns asking and answering questions with a partner. Then write brief notes.

Discussion Frames	Text Notes
Q: What is a **central idea** in this section? **A:** A **central idea** in this section is _____.	• people may be able to become _____
Q: What are the **relevant supporting details** in this section? **A:** (One/An additional) **relevant supporting detail** in this section is _____. **A:** Perhaps the **most relevant supporting detail** in this section is _____.	• Duckworth's research shows that _____ helps in challenging _____ • like other traits, grit can _____ _____ • people can be _____ gritty about certain experiences and tasks • Duckworth is researching how students can be gritty about _____

✏️ **SUMMARIZE**

"Shrink" Section 3 of the text by writing a summary in 40 or fewer words.

CLASS SUMMARY   **WORD COUNT:** _____

Because grit can _____

and be more present in _____ than others,

Duckworth wants to find out how students can _____

about _____

PARTNER SUMMARY   **WORD COUNT:** _____

Grit is _____ and varies depending

on _____ so Duckworth is

_____

can help students _____

 IDENTIFY PRECISE WORDS

Review Section 3 and your *Portfolio* (pp. 260–261) to identify words for your writing.

Topic Words	High-Utility Academic Words
• community college	• exceptionally
•	•
•	•

Student Writing Model

Academic Writing Type

A **formal written summary** provides an objective overview of the topic and important details from an informational text. The writer credits the author, but writes in primarily his or her own words, without including personal opinions.

    A. The **topic sentence** includes the text type, title, author, and topic.
    B. Detail sentences include the important details from the summarized text.
    C. The **concluding sentence** restates the author's conclusion in the writer's own words.

🔍 ANALYZE TEXT

Read this student model to analyze the elements of a formal summary.

> **A**   In the interview titled "Talent Isn't Fixed and Other Mindsets That Lead to Greatness," Jocelyn K. Glei talks to Carol Dweck about a different way of thinking about talent. Glei begins by discussing how people with a fixed mindset believe abilities have limits and avoid challenging tasks. Dweck continues to describe how a growth mindset emphasizes the process, not the person, when it comes to feedback.
>
> **B**   Additionally, she notes that amending criticism with the word "yet" shows how someone can improve through perseverance. Moreover, the interviewee points out that managers with growth mindset training realized that they could nurture talent in their employees, rather than merely judging them. Glei concludes by asking how people can
>
> **C**   change their mindsets, and Dweck says they should view difficulties as learning opportunities.

💬 MARK & DISCUSS ELEMENTS

Mark the summary elements and use the frames to discuss them with your partner.

1. **Number (1–4) the four elements of the topic sentence.** *The topic sentence includes the* _____.

2. **Draw a box around four transition words or phrases.** *One transition (word/phrase) is* _____.

3. **Underline four important details.** *One important detail in this summary is* _____.

4. **Circle four citation verbs.** *One citation verb that the writer uses is* _____.

5. **Star four precise topic words and check four high-utility academic words.** *An example of a (precise topic word/high-utility academic word) is* _____.

Organize a Formal Summary

Prompt | Write a formal summary of "Angela Duckworth and the Research on 'Grit.'"

Guidelines for Paraphrasing Multiple Sentences
Paraphrase related details from a source text by combining key information into one sentence. Replace key words and phrases with synonyms and keep important topic words.

Text Detail 1	Text Detail 2	Text Detail 3
"College can be a difficult and confusing experience even for people who come from college-educated families, but for first-generation students, college is like learning a new language . . ." (Hanford 140).	"When first-generation students come up against obstacles in college, they have no one in their families to turn to for help, says Villanueva" (Hanford 140).	"Many live at home and have family obligations, such as taking care of siblings or grandparents and helping to pay the bills" (Hanford 140).

 PARAPHRASE IDEAS
Combine key information from the three text details above into one detail sentence.

First-generation college students often encounter challenges, such as

(Text Detail 1) _____

(Text Detail 2) _____ and

(Text Detail 3) _____

PLAN KEY IDEAS & DETAILS
State the text information to write a topic sentence.

In the news article titled (title) _____

(author's full name) _____ (citation verb: explores, examines,

discusses) _____ (topic) _____

_____

List four important details from the text using primarily your own words.

1. _____
   _____

2. _____
   _____

3. _____
   _____

4. _____
   _____

Restate the conclusion in your own words.

_____

_____

Write a Formal Summary

Prompt Write a formal summary of "Angela Duckworth and the Research on 'Grit.'"

✏ WRITE A PARAGRAPH

Use the frame to write your topic sentence, detail sentences, and concluding sentence.

A

In the _____ titled _____
　　　　　(text type)　　　　　　　　　　　　　　　　(title)

_____

_____ _____
(author's full name)　　　　　　　　　　　　　　(citation verb)

_____
(topic)

B

_____ begins by _____ that
(Author's last name)　　　　　　　　　　(citation verb + –ing: presenting, arguing)

_____
(1st important detail)

_____

_____

_____

The (author/writer) _____ continues to _____
　　　　　　　　　　　　　　　　　　　　　　　　　　　　　(citation verb, base form: describe, report)

_____
(2nd important detail)

_____

_____

_____

(He/She) _____ _____ further that
　　　　　　　　　　　　　　　　　(present-tense citation verb)

_____
(3rd important detail)

_____

_____

_____

_____ the (author/writer) _____
(Transition)

_____ _____
(present-tense citation verb)　　　　(4th important detail)

_____

_____

_____

C

_____ concludes by _____ that
(Author's last name)　　　　　　　　　(citation verb + –ing: suggesting, emphasizing)

_____
(restate conclusion)

_____

_____

Rate Your Formal Summary

Scoring Guide	
1	Insufficient
2	Developing
3	Sufficient
4	Exemplary

ASSESS YOUR DRAFT

Rate your formal summary. Then have a partner rate it.

1. Does the topic sentence state the text type, title, author, and topic?	Self	1	2	3	4
	Partner	1	2	3	4
2. Did you paraphrase the most important details from the text?	Self	1	2	3	4
	Partner	1	2	3	4
3. Did you use citation verbs to credit the author?	Self	1	2	3	4
	Partner	1	2	3	4
4. Did you use transitions to introduce and sequence details?	Self	1	2	3	4
	Partner	1	2	3	4
5. Did you include precise topic words and high-utility academic words?	Self	1	2	3	4
	Partner	1	2	3	4
6. Did you accurately restate the author's conclusion?	Self	1	2	3	4
	Partner	1	2	3	4

REFLECT & REVISE

Record specific priorities and suggestions to help you and your partner revise.

(Partner) Positive Feedback: I appreciate how you (used/included) _____

_____

_____

(Partner) Suggestion: As you revise your summary, focus on _____

_____

_____

(Self) Priority 1: My summary paragraph needs _____

_____

_____

(Self) Priority 2: I plan to improve my summary by _____

_____

_____

CHECK & EDIT

Use this checklist to proofread and edit your summary.

☐ Did you capitalize the title of the article and proper nouns?

☐ Did you put quotation marks around the title of the article?

☐ Did you use commas appropriately after transitions?

☐ Do simple present-tense verbs end in –s?

☐ Is each sentence complete?

☐ Are all words spelled correctly?

Words to Know

 BUILD WORD KNOWLEDGE

Rate your word knowledge. Then discuss word meanings and examples with your group.

| | ① Don't Know | ② Recognize | ③ Familiar | ④ Know |

Word to Know	Meaning	Examples
1 **demonstration** noun ① ② ③ ④	a _____ or public gathering to _____ something	I went to a **demonstration** to protest _____ _____ Peaceful **demonstrations** in the 1960s sometimes _____ _____ when the police got involved.
2 **nonviolence** noun ① ② ③ ④	the use of _____ means to bring about political or social change	We learned about Martin Luther King Jr. and his belief in **nonviolence** as a way to _____ _____ The police had no reason to _____ _____ _____ because the protestors relied on **nonviolence**.
3 **segregation** noun ① ② ③ ④	the act or practice of keeping people or groups _____	Some schools have **segregation** of male and female students, but others _____ _____ Because our principal believes that the **segregation** of students with learning difficulties is ineffective, we all _____ _____ _____
4 **policy** noun ① ② ③ ④	a _____ or official way of doing something	Our school has a strict **policy** against _____ _____ My **policy** is to never get in a car with a driver who _____ _____

Close Reading

 READ THE TEXT
Read the text *The Brave Boys of Greensboro* (*Issues*, pp. 144–151).

 IDENTIFY STRUCTURE

Dramatic Elements and Structure

Most dramas have **scenes**. Each scene typically takes place in a different time or place or involves different characters. A **flashback** shows an event that happened earlier.

Use the frames to analyze the drama's structure.

1. What is the structure and purpose of Scene 2?

   Scene 2 is a _____ It shows why _____

   _____

2. What incident in the scene makes the boys take action?

   The incident that makes the boys take action is _____

   _____

 ANALYZE CRAFT & STRUCTURE
Use the frames to compare the novel excerpt from *Countdown* with the drama *The Brave Boys of Greensboro*.

3. How do both texts address "heroes of the civil rights movement"?

   Both texts address "heroes of the civil rights movement" by _____

   _____

4. In *Countdown,* why does the author put the text "This little light of mine, I'm gonna let it shine!" in all capital letters and center it?

   The author uses this text formatting to _____

   _____

5. In *The Brave Boys of Greensboro,* what does the dialogue with Mr. Harris in Scene 3 reveal about his character?

   The dialogue with Mr. Harris reveals that his character is _____

   _____

ANALYZE THEME
Use the frames to analyze the drama's theme.

6. How does the Greensboro Four's unwillingness to give up their plan contribute to the drama's theme, or overall message?

   The boys' unwillingness to give up their plan sends the message that _____

   _____

   _____

Academic Discussion

How does having or not having grit affect the way people approach obstacles?

 BRAINSTORM IDEAS

Briefly record at least two ideas in each column using everyday English.

With Grit	Without Grit
• ignore fear	• avoid challenges
•	•
•	•

 ANALYZE WORDS

Complete the chart with precise words to discuss and write about the topic.

Everyday	Precise
facing (verb)	tackling,
give up (verb)	abandon,
useless (adjective)	powerless,

 MAKE A CLAIM

Rewrite two ideas using the frames and precise words. Then prepare to elaborate verbally.

Language to ELABORATE

To exemplify, _____.

Personally, _____.

1. **Frame:** People (with/without) grit approach obstacles by_____ (**verb + –ing:** avoiding, relying, continuing)

   Response: _____

   _____

2. **Frame:** In *The Brave Boys of Greensboro,* _____ (**character's name**) approaches obstacles by _____ (**verb + –ing:** confronting, risking, ignoring)

   Response: _____

   _____

 COLLABORATE

Listen attentively, restate, and record your partner's ideas.

Language to RESTATE

In other words, your stance is that _____.

Yes, that's accurate.

No. What I intended to say was _____.

Classmate's Name	Ideas
	1.
	2.

Ten-Minute Paper

A **ten-minute paper** begins with a **claim,** followed by **two detail sentences** that elaborate with relevant examples and precise words.

PRESENT IDEAS

Listen, compare ideas, and take notes. Then indicate if you agree (+) or disagree (–).

Classmate's Name	Idea	+/–

ELABORATE IN WRITING

Work with a partner to write a ten-minute paper.

> People without grit approach obstacles by withdrawing from the situation.
>
> For example, many people without grit believe that they are
>
> _____ and do not _____
>
> In *The Brave Boys of Greensboro,* the counter maid demonstrates this when she
>
> _____
>
> because she does not want the boys to _____
>
> _____

Write a ten-minute paper.

> People _____ grit approach obstacles by _____
>
> _____
>
> For example, many people _____ grit are likely to _____
>
> _____
>
> and _____
>
> In *The Brave Boys of Greensboro,* _____ demonstrates this
>
> when _____
>
> _____

Take a Stand

Debate | Is resilience more important for success than intelligence?

 COLLABORATE

Read the debate question about success. Then take turns using a frame to respond with your initial reaction.

Language to RESPOND
So, _____, what's your initial reaction?
My initial reaction is _____.
My initial reaction is related to _____'s.

ANALYZE SOURCES

Read a quote that either supports or opposes the debate question. Then paraphrase.

Quote	Paraphrase
Model: "The grittiest students—not the smartest ones—had the highest GPAs" (Hanford 137).	This quote makes it evident that students with the most _____ have the best _____
1. "But if you're always managing your image to look smart, you're not taking on the hardest tasks, you're not thinking about them in the most innovative ways, and you're not sticking to things that don't work right away" (Glei 133).	In this quote, the author makes a case that a _____ prevents people from _____ and _____
2. "Duckworth's research suggests that when it comes to high achievement, grit may be as essential as intelligence" (Hanford 136).	This quote makes it evident that _____ is _____ important as _____ in terms of _____
3. "At the Scripps National Spelling Bee, the grittiest contestants were the most likely to advance to the finals—at least in part because they studied longer, not because they were smarter or were better spellers" (Hanford 137).	This quote makes it evident that _____ was more important than _____ in a spelling competition.
4. "Many factors contribute to college success, including money, what colleges students go to, and what Duckworth calls 'social-psychological' barriers" (Hanford 139).	In this quote, the author makes a case that factors other than _____ affect success, such as _____ and _____

Debate Ideas

SYNTHESIZE IDEAS

Write a response to the debate question, including a paraphrase of a text quote and elaboration on the quote.

Claim: My position is that resilience (is/is not) _____ more

important for success than intelligence.

Transitional Statement: I have (one key reason/a compelling reason) _____

_____ for taking this stance.

Quote Paraphrase: (According to _____,/The author points out _____.)

_____

_____

_____

Quote Elaboration: (As a result, _____./Consequently, _____.)

_____

_____

_____

PRESENT EVIDENCE

Including Digital Media

When presenting ideas during class or in a meeting, include **digital media.** Consider including images, graphics, audio, or video to express information, strengthen claims and evidence, and add interest.

LISTEN & TAKE NOTES

Listen attentively and take notes. Then indicate if you agree (+) or disagree (–).

> **Language to AFFIRM & CLARIFY**
>
> That's a thought-provoking point of view.
>
> Could you clarify what you mean by _____?

Classmate's Name	Idea	+/–

Student Writing Model

Academic Writing Type

An **argument** states a claim and supports it with logical reasons and relevant evidence from sources.

A. The **thesis statement** clearly states the writer's claim and tells what the writer will explain about the topic.

B. **Supporting paragraphs** support the claim with reasons and evidence from sources. The writer also presents counterclaims and responds with evidence.

C. The **conclusion** restates the writer's claim about the issue.

ANALYZE TEXT
Read this student model to analyze elements of an argument research paper.

A
After reviewing the evidence on the relationship between resilience, intelligence, and success, I am convinced that resilience is not a more important trait than intelligence in terms of achievement.

B
One reason I maintain this position is that so many other factors are involved when it comes to why some people ultimately find success. In "Angela Duckworth and the Research on 'Grit,'" Emily Hanford emphasizes that college success depends on students' financial situations and choice of college (139). She points out that "college can be a difficult and confusing experience" and as a teen, I have firsthand experience with failing in an unfamiliar environment (140). As an illustration, I had a summer internship, but I struggled to fit in due to office politics. In contrast, Hanford's article claims that the grittiest students have better grades than the smartest ones (137). However, I believe that more research is needed.

Scholastic Scope's findings have also strengthened my perspective that intelligence could still be at the heart of many successes attributed to resilience. For example, Steve Jobs and Jeremy Lin are quite intelligent, which may have contributed to their successes (130). Although a common argument in favor of resilience over intelligence is that less intelligent people succeed by working harder to compensate for what they lack, I don't find the evidence convincing (Hanford 136–137). Clearly, there is striking evidence that proves that many people, such as Albert Einstein, became successful because they have formidable intelligence.

C
The question of whether or not resilience has more impact on success than intelligence is intriguing. My analysis of this issue has left me with little doubt that resilience cannot make up for a lack of brainpower.

MARK & DISCUSS ELEMENTS
Mark the argument elements and use the frames to discuss them with your partner.

1. **Circle the writer's claim within the thesis statement.** *The writer's claim is _____.*

2. **Underline and label two reasons that support the writer's claim with the letter R.** *One reason that supports the writer's claim is _____.*

3. **Underline and label four pieces of evidence that support the writer's claim with the letter E.** *One piece of evidence that supports the writer's claim is _____.*

4. **Draw boxes around two counterclaims.** *One counterclaim is _____.*

5. **Star four precise topic words and check four high-utility academic words.** *An example of a (precise topic word/high-utility academic word) is _____.*

Scoring Guide	
1	Insufficient
2	Developing
3	Sufficient
4	Exemplary

ASSESS A STUDENT SAMPLE
Read an additional student writing sample and rate it.

1. Does the thesis statement clearly state the claim?	1	2	3	4
2. Do supporting paragraphs begin with a topic sentence that specifies a reason?	1	2	3	4
3. Did the writer give evidence drawn primarily from sources to support the claim?	1	2	3	4
4. Did the writer explain why the evidence is relevant and significant?	1	2	3	4
5. Did the writer include complex sentences to present and respond to counterclaims?	1	2	3	4
6. Did the writer use strong verbs and verb phrases to express opinions?	1	2	3	4
7. Did the writer use transitions to introduce reasons and evidence?	1	2	3	4
8. Did the writer use precise adjectives to describe evidence?	1	2	3	4
9. Did the writer include citation information for text evidence?	1	2	3	4
10. Did the writer include precise topic words and high-utility words?	1	2	3	4
11. Does the conclusion strongly restate the claim using new wording?	1	2	3	4

REFLECT & REVISE
Record specific priorities and suggestions to help the writer.

I appreciated the student's (effort to/use of/skillful) _____

_____

_____

One suggestion I have to revise this argument research paper is to _____

_____

_____

Another suggestion I have to strengthen this argument research paper is to _____

_____

_____

Noun Phrases to Describe Evidence

Guidelines for Using Noun Phrases to Describe Evidence

Use **noun phrases** to describe the data, statistics, and other evidence you present to support your claim.

Everyday Words	Noun Phrases
a lot of	a/the high percentage of
many	a/the high number of
more	an/the increase in
little/few	a/the low percentage of, a/the limited number of
less	a/the decrease in

WRITE NOUN PHRASES
Complete the sentences with noun phrases.

1. I am in favor of making world-language study a requirement for graduation due to _____ of colleges that only accept applicants who have studied a foreign language.

2. Proponents of mandatory voting contend that it would remedy _____ _____ voter turnout that has been evident since the 1950s.

3. Clearly, there is substantial evidence that shows _____ _____ people claim bankruptcy before the age of 25.

Use noun phrases to complete the sentences about the claim.
Claim: States should increase the minimum driving age.

1. **Evidence:** In "DN'T TXT N DRV," Nancy Mann Jackson emphasizes that _____ _____ vehicle crashes can be linked to teens, who are more likely to be distracted while driving.

2. **Evidence:** To illustrate, _____ teen drivers admitted to texting behind the wheel.

3. **Counterclaim:** Although a common argument against raising the driving age is _____ _____ vehicle crashes involving inexperienced 18-year-old drivers, I don't find the evidence compelling.

4. **Response to Counterclaim:** Clearly, there is striking evidence that shows _____ _____ teen car accidents in states that have raised the driving age.

5. **Restating Claim:** My analysis of this issue has left me with little doubt that _____ _____ fatal car accidents due to teen drivers would result from raising the driving age.

Complex Cause & Effect Sentences

Guidelines for Expressing Cause & Effect

A **cause** is the reason something happens. An **effect** is the result, or what happens.

> *Teens are sleep deprived. Teens may lose focus in class.*
> cause   effect

After stating an effect, use **because** or **since** to signal that the cause follows.

> *Teens may lose focus in class **because** they are sleep deprived.*
> effect   cause

Use **due to** or **as a result of** when you want to state the cause with a noun phrase.

> *Teens may suffer from serious health problems **due to** a lack of sleep.*
> effect   cause

> *Memory loss is common among teens **as a result of** not getting enough sleep.*
> effect   cause

State the cause first to emphasize it. Begin with **because, since, due to,** or **as a result of** and put a comma after the cause.

> ***Because** teens are sleep deprived, they may lose focus in class.*
> cause   effect

WRITE COMPLEX SENTENCES
Combine simple sentences to create complex cause and effect sentences.

1. Learning another language can improve grades. Bilingualism increases cognitive abilities.

   a) _____ because
   _____

   b) Because _____
   _____

2. Many young people cannot manage their money. Many young people claim bankruptcy.

   a) _____ due to
   _____

   b) Due to _____
   _____

3. Schools don't teach job skills. Many high school graduates are unemployed.

   a) _____ as a result of
   _____

   b) As a result of _____
   _____

4. Copying answers from websites is easy. Many online students commit plagiarism.

   a) _____ since
   _____

   b) Since _____
   _____

Organize an Argument

Prompt | Is resilience more important for success than intelligence? Write an argument that states your claim and supports it with text evidence.

Guidelines for Citing Text Evidence

Paraphrase text evidence when you want to summarize a longer section of text or multiple ideas. Use **direct quotes** when the author has used strong wording that is difficult to improve or simplify.

Quote	Cited Evidence
"But Duckworth thinks grit is likely a significant factor when it comes to college completion among the charter school students she is studying" (Hanford 139–140).	Angela Duckworth suspects that grit affects which charter students graduate from college (Hanford 139).
"...what Duckworth has found is that a person's grit score is highly predictive of achievement under challenging circumstances" (Hanford 137).	Duckworth's research shows that people with more grit are more likely to achieve "under challenging circumstances" (Hanford 137).

WRITE A THESIS STATEMENT
Describe your claim.

My claim: _____

Use academic language to restate your claim as a thesis statement.

_____ failure and success,
(Thesis starter)

I _____ that _____
(verb/verb phrase to express opinion)   (strongly state your claim)

_____

CHOOSE SUPPORTING TOPICS
List each topic you will write about to support your claim.

Supporting Paragraph 1

Topic: _____

_____

Supporting Paragraph 2

Topic: _____

_____

Find text evidence that supports your claim and write a sentence that paraphrases it or incorporates a direct quote.

_____

_____

_____

PLAN SUPPORTING PARAGRAPHS
List reasons and evidence that support your claim. You may draw from texts, your experience, or a classmate's experience.

Supporting Paragraph 1:

Reason 1: _____

_____

Evidence: _____

_____

Source/Page Number: _____

Author: _____

Counterclaim 1: _____

_____

Response to Counterclaim: _____

_____

Source/Page Number: _____

Author: _____

Supporting Paragraph 2:

Reason 2: _____

_____

Evidence: _____

_____

Source/Page Number: _____

Author: _____

Counterclaim 2: _____

_____

Response to Counterclaim: _____

_____

Source/Page Number: _____

Author: _____

WRITE A CONCLUSION
Plan a conclusion that restates your claim.

The question of whether or not to _____
(restate the issue)

_____ is _____
(precise adjective to respond)

My analysis of this issue has left me with little doubt that _____
(restate your claim)

_____

Write an Argument

Prompt | Is resilience more important for success than intelligence? Write an argument that states your claim and supports it with text evidence.

 WRITE A RESEARCH PAPER
Use the frame to write your thesis statement, supporting paragraphs, and conclusion.

A

(Thesis starter)

(topic)

I _____
   (verb/verb phrase to express opinion)

that _____
     (strongly state your claim)

B1

One reason I maintain this position is that _____
                                            (1st reason that supports your claim)

In _____
   (title of source)

_____ emphasizes that _____
(author's full name)   (evidence from source)

As a teen, I have firsthand experience with _____
                                             (situation or issue)

_____   _____
(Transition introducing evidence)   (evidence from your experience)

In contrast, _____
             (group with an opposing claim)

_____ that _____
(verb/verb phrase to express opinion)   (counterclaim from source or your experience)

However, I _____ that _____
           (verb/verb phrase to express opinion)   (your response to the counterclaim)

B2

_____ analysis of _____
(Author's full name + 's)   (topic)

_____

in _____
(title of a different source)
has strengthened my perspective that _____
(2nd reason that supports your claim)

_____

_____

(Transition introducing evidence)   (evidence from source or your experience)

_____

_____

_____

_____

Although a common argument (in favor of/against) _____

_____
(issue)
is _____
(counterclaim from source or your experience)

_____

I don't find the evidence (adjective: compelling, substantial) _____

_____ Clearly, there is (adjective: sufficient, adequate, striking)

_____ evidence that (shows/proves) _____

(your response to the counterclaim)

_____

_____

C

The question of whether or not to _____
(restate the issue)

_____

_____ is _____
(precise adjective to respond)

My analysis of this issue has left me with little doubt that _____
(restate your claim)

_____

_____

_____

Two-Minute Speech

IDENTIFY TOPIC
Choose one of the questions below to address in a two-minute speech.

☐ Should our city require everyone to vote in local elections?

☐ Should our school grade students on effort rather than on results?

BRAINSTORM IDEAS
Write your position and two reasons that support it.

My Claim: _____

Reason 1: _____

Reason 2: _____

SYNTHESIZE IDEAS
Take notes on supporting evidence and a counterclaim.

Evidence 1: _____

_____

Evidence 2: _____

_____

Counterclaim: _____

_____

Response: _____

_____

WRITE A SPEECH
Write a two-minute speech that states your claim and includes reasons, evidence, and a counterclaim.

From my point of view, _____

_____

One reason is that _____

_____

Secondly, _____

_____

For example, _____

_____

Critics might claim that _____

_____

However, _____

_____

For these reasons, I _____ that _____

_____

Present & Rate Your Speech

Including Digital Media
When presenting ideas during class or in a meeting, include **digital media.** Consider including images, graphics, audio, or video to express information, strengthen claims and evidence, and add interest.

PRESENT YOUR SPEECH
Present your speech to the small group. Make sure to include digital media.

LISTEN & TAKE NOTES
Listen attentively and take notes. Then indicate if you agree (+) or disagree (–).

Language to AFFIRM & CLARIFY
That's a thought-provoking point of view.
Could you clarify what you mean by _____?

Classmate's Name	Idea	+/–

ASSESS YOUR SPEECH
Use the Scoring Guide to rate your speech.

Scoring Guide			
1	Insufficient	3	Sufficient
2	Developing	4	Exemplary

1. Did your topic sentence clearly state your claim?	1	2	3	4
2. Did you include strong reasons and evidence to support your speech?	1	2	3	4
3. Did you include precise topic words?	1	2	3	4
4. Were you easy to understand?	1	2	3	4
5. Did you include digital media?	1	2	3	4

REFLECT
Think of two ways you have improved on your speeches.

Priority 1: In my speeches, I was successful with _____
_____
_____

Priority 2: My greatest area of improvement was _____
_____
_____

Completing the Daily Do Now

DAILY DO NOW ROUTINE

Follow these steps each day when you enter class:

1. Turn to the Daily Do Now in your *Language & Writing Portfolio* and record the date.

2. Read the task on the board, think carefully, and write an appropriate response.

3. Listen to classmates share their responses and share your response if asked.

4. Score your response using the Scoring Guide.

5. Read your response aloud to your partner.

6. Switch *Language & Writing Portfolios* with your partner and score his or her response.

DAILY DO NOW TYPES

There are two types of Daily Do Nows. Complete the Daily Do Now according to the type of task.

Show You Know

Example: (advantage) One ____ of living near school is being able to ____.

- Write the correct form of the word in one of the blanks. If it is a noun, you may need to make it plural (often by adding *–s* or *–es*). If it is a verb, you may need to change its tense (often by adding *–ed* or *–s*).

- Complete the rest of the sentence with content that shows you understand the word's meaning.

Date 9 / 23 / 13			Self
One advantage of living near school is being able to sleep later in the mornings.			Partner

Academic Talk

Example: Students who are <u>not getting enough sleep</u> often feel <u>very tired</u> during ____.

- Replace the underlined words or phrases with academic words you would use to communicate with the principal or an employer.

- Complete the rest of the sentence with content that shows you understand the word's meaning.

Date 10 / 21 / 13			Self
Students who are sleep deprived often feel fatigued during morning classes.			Partner

Scoring the Daily Do Now

DETERMINING A SCORE

Use this rubric and the Scoring Guide to score your Daily Do Nows. Record two points for accurate use of vocabulary and one point for each of the other elements.

	Complete Do Now	Use Vocabulary	Add Content	Correct Grammar
Points	1	2	1	1
Show You Know	Copied the sentence and completed the blank(s)	Used cues in the sentence to write the correct form of the word	Added relevant content that shows understanding of the word meaning	Completed the sentence using correct grammar
Academic Talk	Copied the sentence, replaced the underlined words, and completed the blank	Used accurate, precise synonyms to replace the underlined everyday words	Added relevant content that shows understanding of the word meaning	Substituted words that are the same part of speech and agree with the sentence

CALCULATING A GRADING TOTAL

At the end of each Issue, calculate your Grading Total by dividing the Total Points by the Possible Points and then multiplying by 100.

	Total Points	Possible Points	Grading Total (Total Points/Possible Points X 100)
Getting Started			
Issue 1			
Issue 2			
Issue 3			
Issue 4			
Issue 5			
Issue 6			
Issue 7			
Issue 8			

Insufficient	Developing	Admirable	Exceptional
0–50%	51–70%	71–90%	91–100%

Daily Do Now

Record the Daily Do Now at the beginning of each class. Complete the task using appropriate content, precise vocabulary, and correct grammar.

	Scores					
	Complete Do Now	Use Vocabulary	Add Content	Correct Grammar	Total	
Date ____ / ____ / _____						Self
						Partner
Date ____ / ____ / _____						Self
						Partner
Date ____ / ____ / _____						Self
						Partner
Date ____ / ____ / _____						Self
						Partner
Date ____ / ____ / _____						Self
						Partner
Total Points						

Scoring Guide	Self	Partner
Did you/your partner **complete** the Daily Do Now?	+1	+1
Did you/your partner **use vocabulary** accurately?	+2	+2
Did you/your partner **add content** that is relevant?	+1	+1
Did you/your partner **use correct grammar**?	+1	+1

	Scores				
Complete Do Now	Use Vocabulary	Add Content	Correct Grammar	Total	

Date _____ / _____ / _____
_____
_____
_____
_____

Self

Partner

Date _____ / _____ / _____
_____
_____
_____
_____

Self

Partner

Date _____ / _____ / _____
_____
_____
_____
_____

Self

Partner

Date _____ / _____ / _____
_____
_____
_____
_____

Self

Partner

Date _____ / _____ / _____
_____
_____
_____
_____

Self

Partner

Total Points

Daily Do Now

Record the Daily Do Now at the beginning of each class. Complete the task using appropriate content, precise vocabulary, and correct grammar.

	Scores				
	Complete Do Now	Use Vocabulary	Add Content	Correct Grammar	Total

Date _____ / _____ / _____

_____

_____

_____

_____

Self

Partner

Date _____ / _____ / _____

_____

_____

_____

_____

Self

Partner

Date _____ / _____ / _____

_____

_____

_____

_____

Self

Partner

Date _____ / _____ / _____

_____

_____

_____

_____

Self

Partner

Date _____ / _____ / _____

_____

_____

_____

_____

Self

Partner

Total Points

Scoring Guide

Scoring Guide	Self	Partner
Did you/your partner **complete** the Daily Do Now?	+1	+1
Did you/your partner **use vocabulary** accurately?	+2	+2
Did you/your partner **add content** that is relevant?	+1	+1
Did you/your partner **use correct grammar**?	+1	+1

	Scores					
	Complete Do Now	Use Vocabulary	Add Content	Correct Grammar	Total	
Date ____ / ____ / _____						Self
						Partner
Date ____ / ____ / _____						Self
						Partner
Date ____ / ____ / _____						Self
						Partner
Date ____ / ____ / _____						Self
						Partner
Date ____ / ____ / _____						Self
						Partner
Total Points						

Daily Do Now

Record the Daily Do Now at the beginning of each class. Complete the task using appropriate content, precise vocabulary, and correct grammar.

	Complete Do Now	Use Vocabulary	Add Content	Correct Grammar	Total	
Scores						
Date ____ / ____ / _____						Self
						Partner
Date ____ / ____ / _____						Self
						Partner
Date ____ / ____ / _____						Self
						Partner
Date ____ / ____ / _____						Self
						Partner
Date ____ / ____ / _____						Self
						Partner
Total Points						

Scoring Guide	Self	Partner
Did you/your partner **complete** the Daily Do Now?	+1	+1
Did you/your partner **use vocabulary** accurately?	+2	+2
Did you/your partner **add content** that is relevant?	+1	+1
Did you/your partner **use correct grammar**?	+1	+1

	Scores					
	Complete Do Now	Use Vocabulary	Add Content	Correct Grammar	Total	

Date _____ / _____ / _____

_____

_____

_____

_____

| | | | | | | Self |
| | | | | | | Partner |

Date _____ / _____ / _____

_____

_____

_____

_____

| | | | | | | Self |
| | | | | | | Partner |

Date _____ / _____ / _____

_____

_____

_____

_____

| | | | | | | Self |
| | | | | | | Partner |

Date _____ / _____ / _____

_____

_____

_____

_____

| | | | | | | Self |
| | | | | | | Partner |

Date _____ / _____ / _____

_____

_____

_____

_____

| | | | | | | Self |
| | | | | | | Partner |

Total Points

Daily Do Now

Record the Daily Do Now at the beginning of each class. Complete the task using appropriate content, precise vocabulary, and correct grammar.

	Scores					
	Complete Do Now	Use Vocabulary	Add Content	Correct Grammar	Total	
Date ____ / ____ / _____						Self
						Partner
Date ____ / ____ / _____						Self
						Partner
Date ____ / ____ / _____						Self
						Partner
Date ____ / ____ / _____						Self
						Partner
Date ____ / ____ / _____						Self
						Partner
Total Points						

Scoring Guide	Self	Partner
Did you/your partner **complete** the Daily Do Now?	+1	+1
Did you/your partner **use vocabulary** accurately?	+2	+2
Did you/your partner **add content** that is relevant?	+1	+1
Did you/your partner **use correct grammar**?	+1	+1

	Scores				
	Complete Do Now	Use Vocabulary	Add Content	Correct Grammar	Total

Date ____ / ____ / _____

_____
_____
_____
_____

					Self
					Partner

Date ____ / ____ / _____

_____
_____
_____
_____

					Self
					Partner

Date ____ / ____ / _____

_____
_____
_____
_____

					Self
					Partner

Date ____ / ____ / _____

_____
_____
_____
_____

					Self
					Partner

Date ____ / ____ / _____

_____
_____
_____
_____

					Self
					Partner

Total Points

Daily Do Now

Record the Daily Do Now at the beginning of each class. Complete the task using appropriate content, precise vocabulary, and correct grammar.

	Scores					
	Complete Do Now	Use Vocabulary	Add Content	Correct Grammar	Total	
Date ____ / ____ / _____						Self
						Partner
Date ____ / ____ / _____						Self
						Partner
Date ____ / ____ / _____						Self
						Partner
Date ____ / ____ / _____						Self
						Partner
Date ____ / ____ / _____						Self
						Partner
Total Points						

Scoring Guide

	Self	Partner
Did you/your partner **complete** the Daily Do Now?	+1	+1
Did you/your partner **use vocabulary** accurately?	+2	+2
Did you/your partner **add content** that is relevant?	+1	+1
Did you/your partner **use correct grammar**?	+1	+1

	Scores					
	Complete Do Now	Use Vocabulary	Add Content	Correct Grammar	Total	

Date _____ / _____ / _____
_____
_____
_____
_____

Self

Partner

Date _____ / _____ / _____
_____
_____
_____
_____

Self

Partner

Date _____ / _____ / _____
_____
_____
_____
_____

Self

Partner

Date _____ / _____ / _____
_____
_____
_____
_____

Self

Partner

Date _____ / _____ / _____
_____
_____
_____
_____

Self

Partner

Total Points

Daily Do Now

Record the Daily Do Now at the beginning of each class. Complete the task using appropriate content, precise vocabulary, and correct grammar.

	Scores					
	Complete Do Now	Use Vocabulary	Add Content	Correct Grammar	Total	
Date ____ / ____ / _____						Self
						Partner
Date ____ / ____ / _____						Self
						Partner
Date ____ / ____ / _____						Self
						Partner
Date ____ / ____ / _____						Self
						Partner
Date ____ / ____ / _____						Self
						Partner
Total Points						

Scoring Guide	Self	Partner
Did you/your partner **complete** the Daily Do Now?	+1	+1
Did you/your partner **use vocabulary** accurately?	+2	+2
Did you/your partner **add content** that is relevant?	+1	+1
Did you/your partner **use correct grammar**?	+1	+1

Scores					
Complete Do Now	Use Vocabulary	Add Content	Correct Grammar	Total	

Date _____ / _____ / _____
_____
_____
_____
_____

Self

Partner

Date _____ / _____ / _____
_____
_____
_____
_____

Self

Partner

Date _____ / _____ / _____
_____
_____
_____
_____

Self

Partner

Date _____ / _____ / _____
_____
_____
_____
_____

Self

Partner

Date _____ / _____ / _____
_____
_____
_____
_____

Self

Partner

Total Points

Daily Do Now

Record the Daily Do Now at the beginning of each class. Complete the task using appropriate content, precise vocabulary, and correct grammar.

	Complete Do Now	Use Vocabulary	Add Content	Correct Grammar	Total	
Scores						

Date _____ / _____ / _____
_____
_____
_____
_____

— Self
— Partner

Date _____ / _____ / _____
_____
_____
_____
_____

— Self
— Partner

Date _____ / _____ / _____
_____
_____
_____
_____

— Self
— Partner

Date _____ / _____ / _____
_____
_____
_____
_____

— Self
— Partner

Date _____ / _____ / _____
_____
_____
_____
_____

— Self
— Partner

Total Points

Scoring Guide	Self	Partner
Did you/your partner **complete** the Daily Do Now?	+1	+1
Did you/your partner **use vocabulary** accurately?	+2	+2
Did you/your partner **add content** that is relevant?	+1	+1
Did you/your partner **use correct grammar**?	+1	+1

Scores

Complete Do Now	Use Vocabulary	Add Content	Correct Grammar	Total	

Date _____ / _____ / _____

_____

_____

_____

_____

Self

Partner

Date _____ / _____ / _____

_____

_____

_____

_____

Self

Partner

Date _____ / _____ / _____

_____

_____

_____

_____

Self

Partner

Date _____ / _____ / _____

_____

_____

_____

_____

Self

Partner

Date _____ / _____ / _____

_____

_____

_____

_____

Self

Partner

Total Points

Daily Do Now

Record the Daily Do Now at the beginning of each class. Complete the task using appropriate content, precise vocabulary, and correct grammar.

	Complete Do Now	Use Vocabulary	Add Content	Correct Grammar	Total	
Scores						
Date ____ / ____ / _____						Self
						Partner
Date ____ / ____ / _____						Self
						Partner
Date ____ / ____ / _____						Self
						Partner
Date ____ / ____ / _____						Self
						Partner
Date ____ / ____ / _____						Self
						Partner
Total Points						

Scoring Guide	Self	Partner
Did you/your partner **complete** the Daily Do Now?	+1	+1
Did you/your partner **use vocabulary** accurately?	+2	+2
Did you/your partner **add content** that is relevant?	+1	+1
Did you/your partner **use correct grammar**?	+1	+1

	Scores					
	Complete Do Now	Use Vocabulary	Add Content	Correct Grammar	Total	

Date _____ / _____ / _____

_____

_____

_____

_____

Self

Partner

Date _____ / _____ / _____

_____

_____

_____

_____

Self

Partner

Date _____ / _____ / _____

_____

_____

_____

_____

Self

Partner

Date _____ / _____ / _____

_____

_____

_____

_____

Self

Partner

Date _____ / _____ / _____

_____

_____

_____

_____

Self

Partner

Total Points

Daily Do Now

Record the Daily Do Now at the beginning of each class. Complete the task using appropriate content, precise vocabulary, and correct grammar.

	Scores				
	Complete Do Now	Use Vocabulary	Add Content	Correct Grammar	Total

Date ____ / ____ / _____

Self

Partner

Date ____ / ____ / _____

Self

Partner

Date ____ / ____ / _____

Self

Partner

Date ____ / ____ / _____

Self

Partner

Date ____ / ____ / _____

Self

Partner

Total Points

Scoring Guide

	Self	Partner
Did you/your partner **complete** the Daily Do Now?	+1	+1
Did you/your partner **use vocabulary** accurately?	+2	+2
Did you/your partner **add content** that is relevant?	+1	+1
Did you/your partner **use correct grammar**?	+1	+1

Scores

	Complete Do Now	Use Vocabulary	Add Content	Correct Grammar	Total	
Date ____ / ____ / _____						Self
						Partner
Date ____ / ____ / _____						Self
						Partner
Date ____ / ____ / _____						Self
						Partner
Date ____ / ____ / _____						Self
						Partner
Date ____ / ____ / _____						Self
						Partner
Total Points						

Daily Do Now

Record the Daily Do Now at the beginning of each class. Complete the task using appropriate content, precise vocabulary, and correct grammar.

	Complete Do Now	Use Vocabulary	Add Content	Correct Grammar	Total	
Date ____ / ____ / _____						Self
						Partner
Date ____ / ____ / _____						Self
						Partner
Date ____ / ____ / _____						Self
						Partner
Date ____ / ____ / _____						Self
						Partner
Date ____ / ____ / _____						Self
						Partner
Total Points						

Scores

Scoring Guide

	Self	Partner
Did you/your partner **complete** the Daily Do Now?	+1	+1
Did you/your partner **use vocabulary** accurately?	+2	+2
Did you/your partner **add content** that is relevant?	+1	+1
Did you/your partner **use correct grammar**?	+1	+1

Scores

	Complete Do Now	Use Vocabulary	Add Content	Correct Grammar	Total	

Date _____ / _____ / _____

| | | | | | | Self |
| | | | | | | Partner |

Date _____ / _____ / _____

| | | | | | | Self |
| | | | | | | Partner |

Date _____ / _____ / _____

| | | | | | | Self |
| | | | | | | Partner |

Date _____ / _____ / _____

| | | | | | | Self |
| | | | | | | Partner |

Date _____ / _____ / _____

| | | | | | | Self |
| | | | | | | Partner |

Total Points

Daily Do Now

Record the Daily Do Now at the beginning of each class. Complete the task using appropriate content, precise vocabulary, and correct grammar.

	Complete Do Now	Use Vocabulary	Add Content	Correct Grammar	Total	
				Scores		
Date ____ / ____ / _____						Self
						Partner
Date ____ / ____ / _____						Self
						Partner
Date ____ / ____ / _____						Self
						Partner
Date ____ / ____ / _____						Self
						Partner
Date ____ / ____ / _____						Self
						Partner
Total Points						

Scoring Guide

Scoring Guide	Self	Partner
Did you/your partner **complete** the Daily Do Now?	+1	+1
Did you/your partner **use vocabulary** accurately?	+2	+2
Did you/your partner **add content** that is relevant?	+1	+1
Did you/your partner **use correct grammar**?	+1	+1

Scores

	Complete Do Now	Use Vocabulary	Add Content	Correct Grammar	Total	

Date _____ / _____ / _____

| | | | | | | Self |
| | | | | | | Partner |

Date _____ / _____ / _____

| | | | | | | Self |
| | | | | | | Partner |

Date _____ / _____ / _____

| | | | | | | Self |
| | | | | | | Partner |

Date _____ / _____ / _____

| | | | | | | Self |
| | | | | | | Partner |

Date _____ / _____ / _____

| | | | | | | Self |
| | | | | | | Partner |

Total Points

Daily Do Now

Record the Daily Do Now at the beginning of each class. Complete the task using appropriate content, precise vocabulary, and correct grammar.

	Scores					
	Complete Do Now	Use Vocabulary	Add Content	Correct Grammar	Total	

Date _____ / _____ / _____

_____

_____

_____ | | | | | | Self

_____ | | | | | | Partner

Date _____ / _____ / _____

_____

_____ | | | | | | Self

_____

_____ | | | | | | Partner

Date _____ / _____ / _____

_____

_____ | | | | | | Self

_____

_____ | | | | | | Partner

Date _____ / _____ / _____

_____

_____ | | | | | | Self

_____

_____ | | | | | | Partner

Date _____ / _____ / _____

_____

_____ | | | | | | Self

_____

_____ | | | | | | Partner

Total Points

Scoring Guide	Self	Partner
Did you/your partner **complete** the Daily Do Now?	+1	+1
Did you/your partner **use vocabulary** accurately?	+2	+2
Did you/your partner **add content** that is relevant?	+1	+1
Did you/your partner **use correct grammar**?	+1	+1

	Scores					
	Complete Do Now	Use Vocabulary	Add Content	Correct Grammar	Total	

Date _____ / _____ / _____
_____
_____
_____
_____

Self

Partner

Date _____ / _____ / _____
_____
_____
_____
_____

Self

Partner

Date _____ / _____ / _____
_____
_____
_____
_____

Self

Partner

Date _____ / _____ / _____
_____
_____
_____
_____

Self

Partner

Date _____ / _____ / _____
_____
_____
_____
_____

Self

Partner

Total Points

Daily Do Now

Record the Daily Do Now at the beginning of each class. Complete the task using appropriate content, precise vocabulary, and correct grammar.

	Complete Do Now	Use Vocabulary	Add Content	Correct Grammar	Total	
Scores						
Date ____ / ____ / _____						Self
						Partner
Date ____ / ____ / _____						Self
						Partner
Date ____ / ____ / _____						Self
						Partner
Date ____ / ____ / _____						Self
						Partner
Date ____ / ____ / _____						Self
						Partner
Total Points						

Scoring Guide	Self	Partner
Did you/your partner **complete** the Daily Do Now?	+1	+1
Did you/your partner **use vocabulary** accurately?	+2	+2
Did you/your partner **add content** that is relevant?	+1	+1
Did you/your partner **use correct grammar**?	+1	+1

	Scores					
	Complete Do Now	Use Vocabulary	Add Content	Correct Grammar	Total	

Date _____ / _____ / _____
_____
_____
_____
_____

Self

Partner

Date _____ / _____ / _____
_____
_____
_____
_____

Self

Partner

Date _____ / _____ / _____
_____
_____
_____
_____

Self

Partner

Date _____ / _____ / _____
_____
_____
_____
_____

Self

Partner

Date _____ / _____ / _____
_____
_____
_____
_____

Self

Partner

Total Points

Daily Do Now

Record the Daily Do Now at the beginning of each class. Complete the task using appropriate content, precise vocabulary, and correct grammar.

	Scores				
	Complete Do Now	Use Vocabulary	Add Content	Correct Grammar	Total

Date _____ / _____ / _____
_____
_____
_____
_____

| | | | | | Self |
| | | | | | Partner |

Date _____ / _____ / _____
_____
_____
_____
_____

| | | | | | Self |
| | | | | | Partner |

Date _____ / _____ / _____
_____
_____
_____
_____

| | | | | | Self |
| | | | | | Partner |

Date _____ / _____ / _____
_____
_____
_____
_____

| | | | | | Self |
| | | | | | Partner |

Date _____ / _____ / _____
_____
_____
_____
_____

| | | | | | Self |
| | | | | | Partner |

Total Points

Scoring Guide

	Self	Partner
Did you/your partner **complete** the Daily Do Now?	+1	+1
Did you/your partner **use vocabulary** accurately?	+2	+2
Did you/your partner **add content** that is relevant?	+1	+1
Did you/your partner **use correct grammar**?	+1	+1

Scores					
Complete Do Now	Use Vocabulary	Add Content	Correct Grammar	Total	

Date _____ / _____ / _____

_____

_____

_____

_____

| | | | | | Self |
| | | | | | Partner |

Date _____ / _____ / _____

_____

_____

_____

_____

| | | | | | Self |
| | | | | | Partner |

Date _____ / _____ / _____

_____

_____

_____

_____

| | | | | | Self |
| | | | | | Partner |

Date _____ / _____ / _____

_____

_____

_____

_____

| | | | | | Self |
| | | | | | Partner |

Date _____ / _____ / _____

_____

_____

_____

_____

| | | | | | Self |
| | | | | | Partner |

Total Points

Daily Do Now

Record the Daily Do Now at the beginning of each class. Complete the task using appropriate content, precise vocabulary, and correct grammar.

	Complete Do Now	Use Vocabulary	Add Content	Correct Grammar	Total	
				Scores		
Date ____ / ____ / _____						Self
						Partner
Date ____ / ____ / _____						Self
						Partner
Date ____ / ____ / _____						Self
						Partner
Date ____ / ____ / _____						Self
						Partner
Date ____ / ____ / _____						Self
						Partner
Total Points						

Scoring Guide		Self	Partner
Did you/your partner **complete** the Daily Do Now?		+1	+1
Did you/your partner **use vocabulary** accurately?		+2	+2
Did you/your partner **add content** that is relevant?		+1	+1
Did you/your partner **use correct grammar**?		+1	+1

Scores

	Complete Do Now	Use Vocabulary	Add Content	Correct Grammar	Total	

Date _____ / _____ / _____

					Self
					Partner

Date _____ / _____ / _____

					Self
					Partner

Date _____ / _____ / _____

					Self
					Partner

Date _____ / _____ / _____

					Self
					Partner

Date _____ / _____ / _____

					Self
					Partner

Total Points

Daily Do Now

Record the Daily Do Now at the beginning of each class. Complete the task using appropriate content, precise vocabulary, and correct grammar.

	Scores					
	Complete Do Now	Use Vocabulary	Add Content	Correct Grammar	Total	
Date ____ / ____ / _____						Self
						Partner
Date ____ / ____ / _____						Self
						Partner
Date ____ / ____ / _____						Self
						Partner
Date ____ / ____ / _____						Self
						Partner
Date ____ / ____ / _____						Self
						Partner
Total Points						

Scoring Guide

Scoring Guide	Self	Partner
Did you/your partner **complete** the Daily Do Now?	+1	+1
Did you/your partner **use vocabulary** accurately?	+2	+2
Did you/your partner **add content** that is relevant?	+1	+1
Did you/your partner **use correct grammar**?	+1	+1

Scores

	Complete Do Now	Use Vocabulary	Add Content	Correct Grammar	Total	
Date ____ / ____ / _____						Self
						Partner
Date ____ / ____ / _____						Self
						Partner
Date ____ / ____ / _____						Self
						Partner
Date ____ / ____ / _____						Self
						Partner
Date ____ / ____ / _____						Self
						Partner
Total Points						

Daily Do Now

Record the Daily Do Now at the beginning of each class. Complete the task using appropriate content, precise vocabulary, and correct grammar.

	Scores					
	Complete Do Now	Use Vocabulary	Add Content	Correct Grammar	Total	
Date ____ / ____ / _____						Self
						Partner
Date ____ / ____ / _____						Self
						Partner
Date ____ / ____ / _____						Self
						Partner
Date ____ / ____ / _____						Self
						Partner
Date ____ / ____ / _____						Self
						Partner
					Total Points	

Scoring Guide	Self	Partner
Did you/your partner **complete** the Daily Do Now?	+1	+1
Did you/your partner **use vocabulary** accurately?	+2	+2
Did you/your partner **add content** that is relevant?	+1	+1
Did you/your partner **use correct grammar**?	+1	+1

	Scores					
	Complete Do Now	Use Vocabulary	Add Content	Correct Grammar	Total	

Date _____ / _____ / _____
_____
_____
_____
_____

Self

Partner

Date _____ / _____ / _____
_____
_____
_____
_____

Self

Partner

Date _____ / _____ / _____
_____
_____
_____
_____

Self

Partner

Date _____ / _____ / _____
_____
_____
_____
_____

Self

Partner

Date _____ / _____ / _____
_____
_____
_____
_____

Self

Partner

Total Points

Daily Do Now

Record the Daily Do Now at the beginning of each class. Complete the task using appropriate content, precise vocabulary, and correct grammar.

	Scores					
	Complete Do Now	Use Vocabulary	Add Content	Correct Grammar	Total	
Date ____ / ____ / _____						Self
						Partner
Date ____ / ____ / _____						Self
						Partner
Date ____ / ____ / _____						Self
						Partner
Date ____ / ____ / _____						Self
						Partner
Date ____ / ____ / _____						Self
						Partner
Total Points						

Scoring Guide	Self	Partner
Did you/your partner **complete** the Daily Do Now?	+1	+1
Did you/your partner **use vocabulary** accurately?	+2	+2
Did you/your partner **add content** that is relevant?	+1	+1
Did you/your partner **use correct grammar**?	+1	+1

	Scores					
	Complete Do Now	Use Vocabulary	Add Content	Correct Grammar	Total	

Date _____ / _____ / _____

| | | | | | | Self |
| | | | | | | Partner |

Date _____ / _____ / _____

| | | | | | | Self |
| | | | | | | Partner |

Date _____ / _____ / _____

| | | | | | | Self |
| | | | | | | Partner |

Date _____ / _____ / _____

| | | | | | | Self |
| | | | | | | Partner |

Date _____ / _____ / _____

| | | | | | | Self |
| | | | | | | Partner |

Total Points